The Oyster & the Eagle

B Moser 1973

The Oyster & the Eagle:

Selected Aphorisms and

Parables of Multatuli

Translated, edited, annotated,

with an Introductory Essay

by E. M. Beekman

University of Massachusetts Press   Amherst 1974

For John Clayton

Introduction

Multatuli is the pseudonym of Eduard Douwes Dekker, Holland's greatest writer of the nineteenth century, the father of contemporary Dutch literature, and
one of the great figures of modern European intellectual history. The German intelligentsia around the turn
of the century considered him an equal of Nietzsche;
Freud counted him among his primary influences; D.H.
Lawrence begrudged admiration; and in the Soviet Union he is even today applauded as a crypto-Marxist.
Anyone can find in Multatuli's work and life a sympathetic idealism—anyone, that is, except an established authority. It is almost impossible to present a
definitive portrait of the man or a definitive interpretation of his work. The most accurate statement one can
make about Multatuli is that he exemplifies paradox.
Yet he was a consequent man and a passionate idealist.

This strange genius was born in Amsterdam in 1820,
one of four children of a sea captain who was seldom
home and who left the rearing of the children to his
wife. Dekker grew up in an uninspiring environment
in an uninspiring time: protestant morality, an inflexi-
ble social hierarchy, and the pursuit of money were the
determining factors in a closed society that tended to
make life seem prefabricated and to fill it with a desperate boredom.

Yet, paradoxically enough, this staid and mundane
nation owned an exotic empire: the colony of the
Dutch East Indies. A vast realm of huge islands several

months' sailing away, tropically lush and ripe, the Indies were the very antithesis to small, compact, northern, inhibited Holland. This peculiar political union,
entirely motivated by profit, has produced strange amal-
gams in a national personality that might otherwise
have remained somewhat pedestrian. The relationship
between Holland and the Indies reminds one somewhat
of Freud's linkage of the restrictive superego and the
uncouth id. To some degree the one always distrusts the
other and the goal is to attain a harmonious conflict
that will not greatly injure either combatant. Or one
could see this uneasy alliance as an example of Thomas
Mann's favorite parentage for artists: the sobriety of
the northern and the license of the exotic. The mind of
Multatuli could well have been the offspring of such a
metaphysical union, but, when he set sail for Java in
1838 on his father's ship, he was still Dekker, an eight-
een-year-old lapsed student, the son of a common man,
who could not quite make it as an apprentice theolo-
gian.

After fifteen weeks of sailing, Dekker arrived in the
Indies in January of 1839; he remained there until
1857. It was during those years in the tropics that the
boy became an adult, that a character was formed, that
intimations of creativity were heeded, that Eduard
Douwes Dekker translated himself into Multatuli.

Dekker came up through the ranks of colonial bureaucracy with some alacrity. From clerk in the general ac-
counting office in Batavia (the capital) he became
Assistant Resident, a position of considerable responsi-
bility, within thirteen years of service—excluding three
years' furlough in Europe. But the competent official,

which Dekker undoubtedly had become, was always at odds with a rebellious spirit that could not allow him simply to comply with legislated sanctions. Dekker could not obey the rules of official conduct since he could not dismiss the human plight of the native population for which he was responsible—administratively as well as morally. And Dekker took his moral charge very seriously, to the point of letting it outweigh loyalty to authority. It is therefore no surprise that Dekker found himself embroiled with his superiors, first in Sumatra and later in the district of Lebak in Java.

It must be emphasized that, despite the romantic rebelliousness in his character, Dekker had the will power to discipline himself in order to handle efficiently the quotidian affairs of his assignments. He demonstrated considerable administrative abilities and, more importantly, he had a flair for getting to know and understand the native populace—the latter obviously a great asset for a colonial administrator.

A feeling of dejection resulting from clashes with his superiors was compounded by an unhappy love affair in Java. Dekker fell in love with a Catholic girl, Caroline Versteegh, who refused to marry him. This emotional adversity hurt him deeply and, coupled with his professional troubles in Sumatra (where he was accused of having embezzled funds—a charge subsequently found to be erroneous), embittered Dekker, though it also forced him to find his own strength without taking refuge in external sources. His feeling of separateness and loneliness fostered the romantic impulse in him as well as an unrelenting will to succeed on his own terms.

In 1845 Dekker met an impoverished woman of

nobility, Everdine van Wijnbergen, whom he married in 1846. In many ways Everdine was the perfect wife for the struggling idealist who was constantly asserting his own genius only to see it ignored time and again. Everdine was a soul in need, had suffered privations, was almost proverbially long-suffering, and literally worshipped the man who was to make her suffer a great deal. But it appears there was some cause for Dekker's subsequent behavior. About not one single aspect of his life could one ever say that Dekker was reserved, cautious, or continent, whereas his wife seems to have been his opposite in personality; his letters to her, from their engagement on, hint at her aversion for physical passion. It was a problematic if not enervating relationship, for, despite her sexual reticence, Everdine was a woman of presence, of dignity, and of unflagging devotion. Dekker was caught in a fine trap: the obligation to concede personal admiration for Everdine—a woman almost irritating in her goodness—was undermined by her physical indifference.

After seven years of marriage their first child, a son, was born in 1854; the second, a girl, followed three years later.

Because of illness Dekker was granted in 1852 a two year furlough in Holland. Just before Christmas, he was back in Amsterdam after thirteen years of life in the tropics. Things had changed. His parents and two of his siblings were dead. He found that he could not live as expensively in Holland as he had done in the Indies, though the experience left him penniless. Furthermore, attempts to become a professional writer were dismissed by publishers who felt that even his early work was unfit for mid-nineteenth-century Dutch taste. After his son was born, with his own physical condition in disrepair and with only the prospect of an administrative career in front of him, Dekker tried desperately (and succeeded) to extend his stay several times and was twice able to wangle an advance on his salary from the government. In late 1854 and early 1855, Dekker tried gambling in several German casinos, convinced that he had a method to beat the system. He lost. Because of lack of money and official pressure he was forced finally to return to the tropics in May 1855. In less than a year Dekker's entire life was to change dramatically and irrevocably.

Dekker's Waterloo was Lebak, a poor district in West Java. In January of 1856 he was appointed Assistant Resident there, an appointment which constituted something of a promotion, though the assignment itself was far from ideal. Lebak had a population of devout Mohammedans who were often in revolt against their Dutch masters. The native nobility was notorious for exploiting its own people and had enjoyed the tacit compliance of the Dutch authorities for some time. Dekker was acquainted with the desperate plight of the local populace who, in effect, had to work three times: once for the Dutch, once for their native masters, and finally, if possible, for themselves. Dekker's predecessor had tried to rectify some of these abuses, but he had died in Lebak under suspicion of having been poisoned.

It became quickly evident that Dekker's main opponent, who was also the worst offender in the exaction of illegally forced labor, was the native monarch, who was both revered and feared by the native population. Characteristically, Dekker took the side of the oppressed majority as he had done during all of his earlier assignments: if consistent in anything, it was in his allegiances. A relatively minor matter became a test of strength. When he found out that a group of men had been illegally required to cut the grass in the native monarch's yard (a bigger task than it may sound, considering the size of tropical yards and the abundance of vegetation), Dekker ordered them to stop their labor and told them to go home. It was a direct affront to the monarch's authority and Dekker had to act swiftly. Supported by proofs from his predecessor's files, plus the complaints of the native population, which could reach his ears only indirectly, and the implication that his former colleague had been murdered in order to punish his meddling, Dekker felt that he had sufficient cause to write to his superiors accusing the native monarch of "misusing his authority to obtain illegal labor from his subjects" and of exacting produce without payment.

In the eyes of the Dutch authorities Dekker had made a cardinal mistake: he had put his grievances black on white, thereby insisting that the matter be officially noticed. Again and again he wrote, each time insisting that appropriate steps be taken to prosecute the native ruler and to redress the miseries of the poor. But what Dekker saw as a clear-cut case of suffering humanity and abuse of power was to his superiors nothing but a very delicate political matter. They looked on Dekker's action as something akin to insubordination, in that he had not gone through proper channels —i.e., Dekker had refused to be discreet and circumspect in the matter, knowing full well that acceptable behavior would bring no result. Dekker was dealt with swiftly and effectively. An official informed him of the government's displeasure, of its decision to remove him from his post, and ordered a reassignment that amounted to administrative punishment. Recourse was denied. Dekker asked for a honorable discharge from governmental service which was granted within one week. He had been in Lebak less than four months.

What could have been no more than a bureaucratic dogfight, turned, four years later, into a *cause célèbre.* The government had won a Phyrric victory but Dekker had found Multatuli. Essentially, the Lebak affair was simply a case of humanitarian principles assailing a colonial hierarchy whose values did not include such luxuries. Reform was a slow and calculated process that was executed by cautious people in a circumspect man-ner. After all, a challenge to the simplicity of oppres-sion and exploitation sounds outrageously idealistic, if not revolutionary, in the chambers of profit. It was the conflict of an ideal based on fact against a realism re-luctant to give the lie to vested interests.

Dekker's position was hopeless. He could not find a job in the system. With countless debts and a wife pregnant with their second child, Dekker saw no other recourse but to leave the tropics and try his luck in Europe. He left his family with his brother and set sail for Europe. He never saw the Dutch East Indies again.

The next period of Dekker's life is somewhat shadowy. First he travelled around in France and Germany. He tried his luck again at gambling, with the previous re-sult. By January 1858 he was in Brussels and took up lodgings in Au Prince Belge in Rue de la Montagne, the very place where Baudelaire stayed during his last attempt at establishing his fame in 1864–65. To make a living Dekker managed to find some journalistic work.

During these years he had also some romantic interests, including one in Kassel (Germany), a very respectable town where he was thought to be a highly placed official with a romantically tragic past. He had to skip the bill of the expensive hotel where he was staying because he had not enough money. This was in January 1859, about the time that his wife and children finally arrived from the tropics. After trekking from city to city in constantly increasing poverty, Everdine found refuge with Dekker's patient brother Jan, who had come back to Holland to retire.

By September of 1859, Dekker was back in Au Prince Belge in Brussels prepared to write an account of his experiences. In one month of incredible creative energy, Dekker wrote the book that made his fame and that is still one of the classics of Dutch literature. It took him another month to copy it, and it was published in May 1860 under the pseudonym Multatuli as *Max Havelaar*.

The book is shaped around a central section that narrates Dekker's experiences in Lebak. Dekker's stand-in is Havelaar, a man whose trials and tribulations in colonial service are narrated in a bundle of papers which a poor man called Scarfman gives to Drystubble, a broker in coffee from Amsterdam. Drystubble has the notion that this manuscript provides him with the chance to tell the world about his troubles as an honest capitalist in a fluctuating world market. With the help of an employee, a romantically inclined apprentice businessman from Germany, Drystubble writes what is the printed book called *Max Havelaar*. But in the final pages Multatuli dismisses his characters and comes to the fore as the courageous reformer who wants to shake the conscience of a nation and who is not afraid to make a direct challenge to his king, William III of Holland.

Besides the immediate political upheaval, the book also created a stir in literary circles. Just as revolutionary in style and form as in content, *Max Havelaar* was the first work of modern Dutch literature. Multatuli mixed colloquial and poetic speech to create a new diction that had not been dared before. Furthermore, he used an idiosyncratic spelling and alternated succinct declarative sentences with breathless, sometimes gasping, passages where emotion seems incapable of fitting into syntactical units. It is a style that marks the man: here is no carefully disguised literary fabrication that excludes the author from contact with his audience. This is a style militant, brusque, passionate, driven by the psyche of the author, a man not afraid to *mis son coeur à nu*. The book dispenses with the rhetorical elegance and circumspection required of ministers' parlors. Common speech is used not simply as an oddity but as a strong vehicle for literary expression: it brings stylistic democracy from a man with aristocratic aspirations. This is a natural style where, to quote Pascal, "on s'attendait de voir un auteur et on trouve un homme."

Max Havelaar is also technically a unicum. It uses every possible method of rhetorical persuasion—a necessary task, since its main function is to convince and cajole. The modes employed include Dickensian satire, realistic description, clerical enumeration of facts and data, political diatribe; the book employs lyrical expostulations, parables, letters, tracts, and a tale with a message in the tradition of such French romantics as Bernardin de St. Pierre, Chateaubriand, and Rousseau.

Despite its motley elements, the book is all of a piece. The relentlessness of the accusatory tone and of the militant criticism gives urgency to the moral simplicity that makes for all good satire: "the Javanese people are being mistreated." Specifically, *Max Havelaar* is Menippean satire. Most of the frustrations of its critics have come from the fact that they try to squeeze the book into the tradition of the novel. A novel, pure and simple, it hardly is, nor does it have the direct and more unified tone of purer examples of satire such as *Candide* or *Gulliver's Travels*. But this very bustle of modes marks it Menippean—a form of satiric fiction that purposely employs a salmagundi of styles and modes. Multatuli's predilection for data, detail, and digressions of a semilearned or intellectual nature underscores the Menippean author's delight in an erudition that wants either to convince or to overwhelm the enemy. It is a book that narrates a mental attitude— an attitude that bears the unmistakable stamp of its creator.

And it is precisely this unity of voice and of focus that, on closer inspection, makes *Max Havelaar* an astonishingly sustained piece of work. Everything in the book reiterates the basic moral position: the mistreatment of the Javanese people. *Max Havelaar* is a collection of kaleidoscopic bits that center on and reflect this midpoint: from the stolid mendacity of Drystubble to the religious viciousness of the minister Wawelaar; from the noble speech to the Heads of Lebak which, in its rhetorical simplicity, stipulates the moral duty of the Dutch official, to the romantic agony of the tale of Saidjah and Adinda and the parable of the Japanese stone cutter that teaches a stoical acceptance of fate.

Though fostered by historical forces, *Max Havelaar* was never destined to be a topical book that would die with time and be shelved as a curiosity. Oppression, if not colonialism, is still very much an issue of the day; on a more important level, the book is the portrait of a moral point of view, one that cannot age unless we have slipped unaware into a beneficent Utopia. Hence Swift's remark on the relative immortality of his main work is perfectly applicable to *Max Havelaar:* "If the volumes of Gulliver were designed only for the British Isles, that traveller ought to pass for a very contemptible writer. The same vices and the same follies reign everywhere; at least in the civilized countries of Europe: and the author who writes only for one city, one province, one kingdom or even one age, does not deserve to be read, let alone translated." Mediocrity, stupidity, base greed for gain, exploitation of those who are weaker and defenseless, the armed confinement of closeted minds—such adversaries will always be found for him who will not condone the way of the world. But moral strictures and political philippics should come from an intellectual generosity. Despite all his contradiction, one must conclude that Multatuli had loftiness of purpose and an intellectual wisdom that were equal to his task.

From 1860 on, Dekker, now permanently transformed into Multatuli (a Latin scramble meaning something like "I have suffered a lot"), was a famous and lionized author. But misfortune kept on dogging him. Despite his fame, he never achieved financial security. *Max Havelaar* was published by a Dutch author who had the book distributed in an expensive edition, thereby effectively diminishing its popular effect. Multatuli had foolishly sold his copyright to this generous soul, and not until 1874 did a more humane and inspired publisher buy the rights back to produce the edition that Multatuli had always envisioned. The book went through five editions during his lifetime, but it did not bring him much money.

Ironically, its posthumous career was more impressive. It appeared three times in French translations, with the 1906 edition prefaced by a statement from Anatole France. The first English translation came out in 1868, though the book never impressed itself on the British mind, as a British notice of Dekker's death indicates: "Max Havelaar, the author of 'Multa Tuli' has died in Germany." In 1927 Knopf published an American edition, with a preface by D.H. Lawrence, that courted more favor. Lawrence completely missed the artistic brilliance of the book, nor did he see the boldness of its technical composition. Nevertheless, that problematic champion of workers and sex had to admit to both a queer fascination and a sense of profundity. After the turn of the century the book was translated into Danish, Swedish, Polish, Russian, Czech, and Slovakian. But Multatuli's real fame was due to a German translation—a tireless effort by Wilhelm Sphor that soon included the major portion of Multatuli's *oeuvre*.

By 1902 a German critic noted that a large number of admirers existed who would elevate Multatuli to a position roughly equivalent or superior to that

1877, finally comprising a total of seven volumes. This work is somewhat reminiscent of Karl Kraus's one-man periodical *Die Fackel*. Multatuli's love for diversity of styles and modes, his penchant for antithetical thought and formulation, his almost constitutional need for contradiction and antitheses—all these factors are voiced in the *Ideeën*.

The *Ideeën* give one the rare opportunity of seeing a writer project his mind without interference in an almost organic process. The salmagundi effect, already noted in *Max Havelaar,* has free rein here: the *Ideeën* contain parables, stories, anecdotes, reminiscences, a somewhat autobiographical and unfinished novel about a child's youth in Amsterdam (a work that was greatly admired by Freud), a five-act play, epigrams, aphorisms, philosophical disquisitions, and plain outcries from the author to his public.

It is a most curious work; unique for his time, it has not lost its impact today. It is still fascinating to hear a strong and passionate voice, in all sorts of modulations, pursue lines of thought that may stop short or go on to brilliant phrases. The virtuosity of Multatuli's style develops in the *Ideeën* unchecked by formal considerations. It is a style that resembles excited, sometimes hysterical speech. Multatuli was reputedly an inspiring orator; here the declamatory style with its peculiar punctuation takes the place of the dramatic tricks that the voice and the body can perform on the podium. Again popular speech mixes comfortably with classical diction, while Multatuli here unleashes his formidable talent for metaphor and simile in a furor of images.

There is a quality of breathlessness about these volumes of *Ideeën* that overwhelms the reader. These pages assault, and Multatuli will let his audience neither nap nor take charge: the reader must be forced to listen, no matter what it is Multatuli has to say. However, the breathlessness of urgency can turn into shortness of breath: few items are formally finished, few trains of thought are followed to the end. It is a work of variation and syncopation, seldom allowing a finished piece; perhaps this is so because the whole work is a solo defiantly refusing to be orchestrated.

Hence it is surprising to find so many brilliant examples of the art of aphorism and parable in Multatuli's work. Aphoristic writing, brought to perfection by the French—especially La Rochefoucauld—is difficult. It requires that the most stringent economy of expression formulate a wide ranging profundity of thought. Aphorisms ask for syntactical control and a mind that has depth, lest the sayings turn into witless musings or topical annotations that resemble yesterday's headlines. Aphorisms of genius aspire to universality, and Multatuli belongs in the company of the select few who had the intellect, wit, and style to render metaphysical complexity into profound simplicity. La Rochefoucauld, Voltaire, Pascal, Lichtenberg, Karl Kraus, Wilde—it is not bad company to keep.

The parable, a Biblical mode, is perhaps even rarer. The parable is a tale that must edify. Its construction is somewhat like a metaphor where the vehicle is stated but the tenor implied. It requires a plastic imagination that can 'picture' thought—a prerequisite Multatuli had almost to excess. That the parable also teaches a militant moralism made it therefore a form well suited to Multatuli's temperament and credo.

Considering the place and the time in which they

were written—the 1860s in Holland—the *Ideeën* contain an astonishing variety of progressive notions, un-
popular at the time, which, in some cases, were not
fully radicalized until a century later. Multatuli spoke
strongly in favor of liberating women from the yokes
of morality, matrimony, and maternity. He felt that
women's minds were being neglected, that conventional
morality bound their feet until they were crippled, and
that society could see women's lives only in terms of
submission to males and the production of children.
He wanted woman to be free in order to pursue her
own inclinations. He criticised the educational system
for educating intelligence and curiosity out of children,
while his hatred of religion stemmed from his belief
that it stultified just about everything admirable in
human existence. Nor could he accept the socio-reli-
gious law that demands respect and love from children
because they happen to be assigned, either by fate or
nature, to an arbitrary set of parents; he believed that
love and affection, be it from women or children, could
not be dictated, only earned. Furthermore, he continued to attack colonial politics, wrote polemics about
Dutch political figures, and castigated the slumbering
literature of his day. One senses that Multatuli, by himself, had taken on the task of being the conscience of
a nation and a people. The precocity of his causes makes
his writings refreshing, especially in comparison to our
contemporary practice of forcefeeding the goose of
liberty with a surfeit of demands.

   Despite genius, despite a host of admirable causes,
despite a fresh and unique style, Multatuli, the most
famous Dutch author of his time, could not make a
living from his work. Like most reformers, he expected

his smashing of idols to result in instant reason and a proliferation of Edens. Over the years the lack of practical results, a failure to get his personal wrongs righted, and his inability to influence anything or anyone of importance, embittered him. The only solace in his prophet's exile was a young woman named Mimi who became his legal wife after Everdine's death in 1874.

His fame and his poverty lured him to strange fancies. Relying on his numerous admirers, Multatuli had himself photographed and the portrait reproduced as both a lithograph and a photograph. The pictures were offered for sale at two different prices, and the anticipated rush was expected to alleviate some of his worst financial troubles. The venture was a fiasco. Nor did the production of his play bring the succor of cash. To make matters worse, he became embroiled with the police one evening when, in a fit of passion, he slapped two men who had been making disparaging remarks about an actress. First he was summoned to appear before a judge, then made to wait so that finally, unwilling to deal with any more pressure, Multatuli rushed off to Germany. He was sentenced to fifteen days in jail in absentia.

Again he hoped that his luck would change in a casino. He sent Mimi, armed with his infallible system, to Homburg with the little money they had. The method failed once more. A description of this system, adorned with character sketches of the types who frequent casinos, was later published as *Millioenen-studiën* (Studies of Millions).

During his exile in Germany Multatuli saw Prussia wage war on Denmark, on Bohemia, and on several German cities and principalities: he found himself witnessing the formation of a unified German empire. To insure himself some sort of steady income he wrote about these events for a Dutch newspaper. When these dispatches became too boring for him, Multatuli began quoting more interesting items from a German newspaper, the *Mainzer Beobachter,* which, as it turned out, was a fiction of his own.

Soon his life took another strange turn. A conservative politician in Holland took seriously both Multatuli's overtures for a position in government and his advice. Suddenly the arch revolutionary found himself invited by a member of government to express his views. Because the prison term still hung over his head, Multatuli could not come to the Dutch capital personally until King William III, despite some strong opposition, granted him amnesty. But once again Multatuli was to be disappointed; his impatient idealism had forgotten his previous troubles with bureaucracy. The politicians deliberated and listened and sat on their thumbs. Nothing happened, one way or another, and Multatuli, shorn of yet another dream—this time political power —went back to Germany.

After much difficulty with unimaginative and moneyminded publishers, Multatuli finally found a brave and sympathetic soul in the publisher G. L. Funke. From 1870 on, Funke gradually bought up the copyrights to the books Multatuli had published with others, issuing them in economical editions and paying his author more commensurate royalties. This change for the better was reflected in Multatuli's increased productivity. The third collection of *Ideeën* appeared in 1870–71, *Millioenen-studiën* in 1873, and *Duizend-en-eenige- hoofdstukken over specialiteiten* (Thousand and One Chapters about

Specialities) in 1871. The latter book is an elegant defense of diversity and rages against the curse of specialization. This concern—still relevant today—can be found throughout his work, even as early as 1851, when he wrote in a letter:

> Imagine Christ saying: "The Kingdom of Heaven is like unto a mustard seed." And the answer: "No—that—is—incorrect.—Mustard seed—is—etc." With a botanical and culinary lecture on mustard. Can't stand it any more.

The relationship with Funke allowed Multatuli for the first time in his life a measure of peace and security. In the 1870s four collections of *Ideeën* were finished; they included the full-length play *Vorstenschool* (School for Kings), which was successfully staged in 1875. During these years his first wife died in Venice and Multatuli married Mimi in 1875, the same year that *Max Havelaar* was finally published intact and augmented with 179 notes. From 1879 to 1881, buoyed by the success of *Vorstenschool* Multatuli went on a lecture tour in Holland. It resulted in even greater fame.

In 1878 Multatuli and his new wife adopted a little German boy whom they named Wouter, after the hero of Multatuli's long and unfinished novel *Woutertje Pieterse*. A belated stroke of luck, a gift from a Maecenas, gave them a house in a small German town, Nieder-Ingelheim: a young admirer of Multatuli, recently married into money, bought it for him as a gift. Multatuli lived there quietly for the rest of his life, financially secure at last with a stipend acquired through the good offices of some influential friends.

But Multatuli did not write any more. The seventh, and last, collection of *Ideeën* had been written very slowly and painfully and had been published in 1871. Thereafter nothing new appeared. The autobiographical novel stops abruptly and remains unfinished, allowing us not even a guess what might have developed. There is something of the silence, though not quite so literal a one, of that other abused genius, Ezra Pound, in the final years of this great Dutch writer. Visited like a shrine—the irritating lot of those who, though great, are ignored or attacked during the years when recognition would have been a welcome stimulant— Multatuli spent the remainder of his life in the company of the little boy, playing chess and writing letters. He died peacefully on 19 February 1887.

The paradox remains. Multatuli was almost systematically contradictory in his thinking and writing, if not in his professions of faith and his personal conduct. He created a style, superbly his own, that set Dutch writing free to enter the modern era. Despite an often bitterly lonely fight, he challenged and tried to demolish Victorian falsehoods and deceptions in mores, politics, and social life. Not merely in one single work, but throughout his entire life, Multatuli bravely championed the cause of the oppressed: colonial peoples, the workers, the poor, women and children. He asked in return only recognition and a financial compensation that would allow him to live decently. He never satisfied anyone: too radical, too humane, too individualistic, too autocratic, too passionate, too innovative, too critical, too reactionary. In other words, Multatuli managed that rare feat of remaining true to himself and honest to his own mind for the extent of a life. He could say with Edmund Burke: "What I have obtained was the fruit of no bargain; the production of no intrigue; the result of no compromise; the effect of no solicitation."

Textual note

These translations were rendered from the collected works of Multatuli: *Volledige Werken,* 7 vols. (Amsterdam: G. A. van Oorschot, 1951–53). Other editions of individual works by Multatuli were also consulted: *Wouterje Pieterse,* ed. G. Stuiveling (Amsterdam: G. A. van Oorschot, 1952), and *Max Havelaar,* ed. M. Bots (Antwerpen: De Nederlandsche Boekhandel, 1965).

Barbertje

[from *Max Havelaar*]

COURT OFFICIAL: Your honor, there stands the man who murdered Barbertje.

JUDGE: That man shall hang. How did he do it?

COURT OFFICIAL: He cut her into small pieces and pickled her.

JUDGE: That was a terribly wrong thing to do. . . . He shall hang for it.

LOTHARIO: Judge, I did not murder Barbertje! I fed her and clothed her and cared for her. . . . I can find witnesses who will testify that I am a good person and not a murderer.

JUDGE: You shall hang! You aggravate your crime with your conceit. It is not fitting for someone who . . . has been accused of something to take himself for a good man.

LOTHARIO: But Judge, there are witnesses who will confirm it. And since I am now accused of murder . . .

JUDGE: You shall hang! You have cut up Barbertje, pickled her, and are satisfied with yourself . . . three capital offenses!

Who are you, my good woman?

WOMAN: I am Barbertje . . .

LOTHARIO: Thank god! Judge, now you can see that I didn't murder her!

JUDGE: Yes . . . well . . . But what about the pickling?

BARBERTJE: No, Judge, he didn't pickle me. On the contrary, he has been very good to me. He is a noble person.

LOTHARIO: There you are, Judge, she says that I am a good person. . . .

JUDGE: Hm . . . the third point still remains. Court Official, take that man, he shall hang. He is guilty of conceit. Clerk, cite in the preamble the judgment of Lessing's patriarch. . . .*

The Japanese Stonecutter

[from *Max Havelaar,* chapter 11]

There was once a man who hewed stones from the rock. His labor was very hard, and he labored much, but his wages were slight and he was not content.

He sighed because his labor was hard, and he cried: Oh, I wish I were rich so I could rest on a couch with a cover of silk.

And an angel came from heaven, saying: You are what you have said.

And he was rich. And he did rest on a couch and the cover was of silk.

And the king of the land went by, with horsemen in front of his carriage. And behind the carriage there were also horsemen and a golden parasol was held over the head of the king.

And when the rich man saw this he was vexed that

---

* Somewhat like a motto, this playlet precedes the first chapter of *Max Havelaar*. It is reminiscent of Büchner's *Woyzeck* in tone and absurd reality. Multatuli refers at the end to the play *Nathan der Weise* by the German writer Gotthold Ephraim Lessing (1729–81). One of the characters is a patriarch who, when asked what should be done with a good man (a Jew who adopted a deserted Christian child and brought it up as his own, though in the Jewish faith), answers that such a man should be burned at the stake.

no golden parasol was held over his own head. And he was not content.

He sighed and cried: I wish to be king.

And an angel came from heaven, saying: You are what you have said.

And he was king. And many horsemen rode in front of his carriage, and there were also horsemen behind his carriage, and a golden parasol was held over his head.

And the sun shone hot rays and scorched the earth so that the grass shoots withered.

And the king complained that the sun burnt his face and that it excelled him in power. And he was not content.

He sighed and cried: I wish to be the sun.

And an angel came from heaven, saying: You are what you have said.

And he was the sun. And he directed his rays upward and down, to the right and to the left, everywhere. And he scorched the grass shoots on earth and the countenances of kings who were on earth.

And a cloud placed itself between him and the earth, and the rays of the sun bounced back from it.

And he grew wroth that his power was resisted and he complained that the cloud excelled him in power. And he was not content.

He wished to be the cloud which was so powerful.

And an angel came from heaven, saying: You are what you have said.

And he became a cloud and placed himself between the sun and the earth, and caught the rays so that the grass grew green.

And the cloud rained large drops on the earth, causing the rivers to swell and floods to carry the herds away.

And he destroyed the fields with much water.

And he fell upon a rock which did not yield. And he splashed in great streams, but the rock did not yield.

And he grew wroth because the rock would not yield and the power of his streams was in vain. And he was not content.

He cried: That rock has been given power which excels mine. I wish to be that rock.

And an angel came from heaven, saying: You are what you have said.

And he did become rock and did not move when the sun shone nor when it rained.

And then there came a man with a pick and with a chisel and with a heavy hammer and he hewed stones out of the rock.

And the rock said: How can it be that this man has power that excels mine and hews stones out of my lap? And he was not content.

He cried: I am weaker than he. . . . I wish to be that man.

And an angel came from heaven, saying: You are what you have said.

And he was a stone cutter. And he hewed stones from the rock, with hard labor, and he labored very hard for small wages, and he was content.

[from *Max Havelaar,* chapter 12]

Just think how often you hear it said: "If that man would only take care of his business, he really would be somebody. But . . ." and then follows the argument that he does not take care of his business and is consequently a nobody. I believe I know the reason for that. Even of the dead we are always told good qualities we hadn't noticed before. I am sure the reason is that they're not in anybody's way. Everybody is more or less a competitor. We would like to subordinate everybody else completely and totally. To say this, however, is forbidden by custom and even by self-interest, for very quickly no one would believe us even though we'd be asserting something that was true.

[from *Max Havelaar,* chapter 12]

We can never be so sure of being praised as when we have a very noticeable defect.

[*Max Havelaar,* note 4]

The oak trunk which is destined to produce smooth dry wood has to begin its existence as a branch full of sap.

First tale of authority

[from *Minnebrieven*]

"Brother, you who are bigger than I, can you reach that pomegranate which smiles at me like an enticing girl amidst those fireblossoms in the green? Look, she has burst from ripeness, and blood-red is the edge of the wound which she herself cut in order to please me! I desire that pomegranate, O brother! You who are bigger than I, stretch out your arm and pluck, so I may eat."

And the big brother did pluck so that his younger brother could eat.

And then he went out into the plain, where he saw a mountain goat who had descended into the depth, seeking her young.

"Have you not seen my lamb?" she was asking a lion, "You who inhabit the plains and know the paths of the fields better than I? They make me weary since I have a cloven hoof."

"Leave your young, your young . . . your lamb, your lamb," said the lion, "and come here so that I can devour you."

And the lion did so.

But the elder brother asked the lion:

"What do you mean, eating a goat who was looking for her young?"

"You heard how she complained about how unfit her hooves were," answered the lion. "Didn't I do the right thing? Look at my claws, which are *fitting;* see how *fit* my teeth are. That is why I ate the goat."

The young man thought about this and looked at his arms, which were long, strong and sturdy. He found them to be so fit . . . that he resolved to force his younger brother to serve him.

From that time on the younger brother served the elder. But he did not rejoice in the discovery which he had the lion to thank for.

And so it has remained to this very day.

Second tale of authority

[from *Minnebrieven*]

Voltaire has said that if God did not exist we would have invented him. Quite right. All power comes from God. He who wants power, wants God. He who needs power or authority makes a God for himself. That's what Moses, Confucius, Zoroaster, Numa,* Columbus, Cortez did. Leaders, augurers, magicians, priests did the same thing. Even today anyone who wants to rule does the same thing. The number of gods is equal to the number of desires. With each new desire a new god.

A servant girl went for a walk with her master's children. She was instructed to guard them well. But look, the children were disobedient and walked away so that her supervision was insufficient and her care idle.

And so she created a black dog out of nothing which would bite any child who didn't stay with her. And the children were afraid of the dog and became very obedient and stayed with her. Consulting her heart she considered the god she had wrought and saw that it was good.

But the children became insane from their fear of the dog. And they still are, up to this very day.

Third tale of authority

[from *Minnebrieven*]

A traveller was laden with gold and silver. Fearing robbers, he supplied himself with weapons. And his serv-

* Numa Pompilius, the second king of Rome and, presumably a historical figure.

ants followed him in great numbers, indeed, there were more of them than all the robbers of the entire country together. He was so well armed and manned that an entire army would not have been able to take his riches away.

Many robbers who did not know this attacked him and would have long regretted it if they hadn't died instantly.

One robber who had become more cautious because of the example of his comrades, consulted a holy hermit who had advice for everything under the sun, because he had for a long time been alone with two bones and a jug of water.

"What should I do, O holy man, in order to become master of the treasures of that traveller?"

"It is very simple," answered the pious hermit. "Throw the snare I will give you around his neck and he will not resist you. He will command his servants to prostrate themselves before you and will give you whatever you desire."

And it came to pass as the holy man had spoken. But the traveller and his companions didn't fare well from it.

That snare was called "religion" and has retained its powers until this very day.

Fourth tale of authority

[from *Minnebrieven*]

"Father, tell me, why doesn't the sun fall down?" The father was ashamed because he did not know why the sun doesn't fall down, and he punished the child because he was ashamed.

The child feared his father's anger and never again asked anything about why the sun does not fall down nor about other things that it wanted to know very badly.

That child never became a man, even though it lived six thousand years . . . no, much longer than that.

It has remained stupid and dull to this very day.

Sixth tale of authority

[from *Minnebrieven*]

For the first time a child was born! The mother was ecstatic and the father also looked upon it with ardent love.

"But, Genius, tell me, will it always stay that small?" asked the mother, and . . . she added:

"I don't know whether I want it to or not. I would gladly see it as big as an adult, but it would also be a shame if it changed so much that I could no longer carry it or feed it with my body."

"Your child will grow to be an adult," said Genius. "It will not keep on feeding itself from you. When it no longer has to be carried by you . . ."

"O Genius", cried the frightened mother, "will my child go away? When it can walk, will it leave me? What must I do to prevent it?"

"Love your child," said Genius, "and it will not leave you."

Which is exactly what happened. And things remained that way for some time. But then many children were born. And for many parents it was bothersome to love all those children.

People discovered a commandment that would replace love, as so many commandments do. Because it was easier to command than to give love.

Honor thy father and thy mother!

The children left their parents as soon as they could walk. A promise was added to the commandment:

That thy days may be long!

A few children stayed with their parents. But they didn't stay in the way the first mother had meant when she asked Genius what she had to do to prevent her child from leaving as soon as it could walk.

And so it has remained to this very day.

Seventh tale of authority

[from *Minnebrieven*]

"The first king was a happy soldier!" said Voltaire, but I am not sure if that's true. It is just as likely, if not more so, that the first king was somebody who knew hermits who distributed snares. But the following tale is true.

Krates was very strong. He could snap a bulwark of tree trunks between his thumb and middle finger and kill thirteen enemies with one blow. When he coughed he caused a fire from the compression of the air, and the moon shook when he thought of movement.

Because of all these virtues Krates became king.

And he died after having been king for some time.

Little Krates, his small son, suffered from rickets, but this did not stop him from wanting to succeed his father, who had been so strong.

He sat down in a chair which he called a *throne,* and cried: "I am king!"

"Why should you be king?" asked the people, who were still stupid and had no notion of succession.

"Well, because my mother lived in the same hut with old Krates who is now dead."

He really said *palace,* but it was actually a hut.

The people didn't understand the implications, and when Krates II called, "Come!" everybody left. But if he said, "Go!" everybody came running.

In short, there was no authority, and Krates II was too stupid to declare that turvy was topsy, as he saw fit.

In one of the opposition newspapers from those days you can read the following: "Why, O Krates II, you who are bowlegged and rash, why do you sit in the chair of the man who lived for twenty years in the same hut with the woman who bore you?

"Get up and make way, and don't say 'Go!' or 'Come!' as if you were the real old Krates! Where are the bulwarks of oak trees you snapped with your fingers? The moon doesn't shake even if you command the universe to split apart. You can't kill a flea, and there isn't a fire anywhere when you sneeze. Get up and make way for someone else who knows all those useful things."

Thus spoke the opposition.

Krates would probably have had to get up from the chair, which he called a throne, if an old nurse had not spoken to the people in the following manner: "Hear me, O people, because I was the nurse of little Krates when he was even smaller than he is now! When he was born his father anointed himself with oil, and behold, a drop of it fell on the head of my foster child. That is why it is not necessary for him to snap walls, nor make the moon shake, nor cause fires by coughing. I say unto you . . ."

But the eloquent nurse did not have to finish. The conclusion was so easily comprehensible that all the people—the editors of the opposition paper the loudest —shouted as if with one voice, *"Long live the anointed of the Lord!"*

And Krates remained sitting on the chair he called a throne.

And he has kept sitting on it, up to this very day.

Eighth tale of authority

[from *Minnebrieven*]

Thugater* milked her father's cows, and indeed she milked well, because what she brought home yielded more butter than the milk brought home by her brothers. I will tell you how this came about and, pay attention, Fancy, so you'll know . . . if ever you have to go out and milk. But I am not telling you this so you can go milk like Thugater, but to point out to you the example of her *brothers* who, by milking less well, did better.

More *cleverly* at any rate.

Before young country folk enter a meadow to milk the cows, much earlier even than that, the cows are already waiting by the fence to be unburdened of the abundance which they really had prepared for their

* Greek for "woman."

calves. But people eat those calves *because it suits them,* and so there is too much milk in the udders. What happens while the cows, with their dumb faces, wait by the fence? When they stand still like that, the lightest part of the milk—the cream, the fat, the butter—floats up and remains, therefore, the farthest removed from the teat.

So he who milks patiently, till the last drop, brings home rich milk. He who is in a hurry leaves the cream behind.

And look, Thugater is *not* in a hurry, but her brothers are. The latter are of the opinion that they have a right to something better than just milking their father's cows. But *she* does not think about such rights.

"My father taught me to shoot with a bow and arrow," said one of the brothers. "I can live by hunting, and I want to wander around the world and work for myself."

"He taught me to fish," said the second. "I'd be crazy if I were always milking for somebody else."

"And he showed me how to make a boat," cried the third. "I cut down a tree, put it in the water and sit on it. I want to know what's to be seen at the other side of the lake."

"I want to live with fair-haired Cune"*, explained the fourth one, "so I'll have a home with my own Thugater to milk for me." And so every brother had a wish, a desire, a *goal.* And they were so absorbed in their own dreams that they didn't give themselves the time to take the cream along with them, and the disconsolate cows had to keep it, without its being of any

* Greek for "daughter."

use to anybody. But Thugater milked to the very last drop.

"Father," the brothers finally cried, "we are *going!*"

"But who will do the milking then?" asked the father.

"Thugater of course!"

"But what if she also develops a taste for boating, for fishing, for hunting and for travelling around the world? What if *she* also gets the idea of living with someone fair or brown, and having her own home with all that goes along with it? You, sons, I can do without, but not *her* . . . because the milk she brings home is so fat." Then the sons, after some deliberation, said: "Father, *don't teach her anything,* and then she'll keep on milking for the rest of her life. Don't show her how a stretched cord, when pulled together, shoots an arrow away. Then she won't have any desire for hunting. Hide from her the habits of fishes, who swallow a sharp hook if it is covered with bait. Then she won't think of casting nets and hooks. Don't teach her how you hollow out a tree so that you can drift away with it to the other side of the lake. Then she won't feel any desire for the other side. And never let her know how, with fair or dark, she can obtain her own home and everything that goes with it. Never let her know any of this, O father, and she will stay with you and the milk of your cows will be creamy! In the meantime let *us* go father, everyone according to his heart's desires." Thus spoke the sons.

But the father, who was a very cautious man, began again, "Pray, what will prevent her from knowing what I don't teach her? What will happen when she sees a bluebottle aboard a floating twig? Or when the drawn thread from her weaving readjusts itself to its previous length and, while contracting rapidly, pushes the bobbin of her loom by chance? Or when at the edge of the brook she sees the fish biting for the wriggling worm but then, misguided by ill-controlled desire, clamps fast to a sharp part of a reed? Or, finally, when she finds the little nest which the larks build in May amidst the clover?"

The sons thought this over again and said, "She'll learn nothing from that father! She is too stupid to create desire from knowledge. We *too* wouldn't have known anything if you hadn't said anything."

But the father answered, "No, she is not stupid. I am afraid that she will learn by herself what you people could *not* learn by yourselves. Thugater is not dumb!"

Then the sons thought about this again, this time more profoundly, and said: "Father, tell her that knowing, understanding and desiring is . . . a sin for a girl!"

This time the cautious father was satisfied.

He let his sons go—go fishing, hunting, travelling around the world, get married—he let them go everywhere. But he forbade knowledge, understanding and desire to Thugater, who innocently kept on milking to the very end.

And so it has remained until this very day.

Ninth tale of authority

[from *Minnebrieven*]

Hassan sold dates in the streets of Damascus. I say he sold them, but I really mean that he didn't sell them, since his dates were so small that no one wanted to buy them. With sorrow and envy he saw how everybody favored the rich Aöuled, who lived next to him on a mat. In Damascus they lived on mats, with a very high ceiling because they had no roofs above their heads. Hence Aöuled's wealth did not consist of houses but of a garden which was fertile, so fertile, in fact, that the dates which grew there were as big as three normal ones. Which was why people bought Aöuled's dates and not Hassan's.

A Derwish came to the city who had too much wisdom and too little food. At any rate, he exchanged his knowledge for food, and you will see how much Hassan profited from this exchange.

"Feed me," commanded the Derwish, "and I will do for you what no Caliph can do. I will force people to buy your dates by making them big, yes, bigger than Aöuled's fruits. . . . How big are they?"

"Alas, Derwish sent by Allah—I kiss your feet— the dates of Aöuled—Allah give him cramps—are three times bigger than normal ones! Come in on my mat, cross your legs, be blessed, and teach me to make my dates big and to force people to buy them."

Hassan could have asked why a Derwish who was so competent would have any need for food, but Hassan never quibbled. He served his guest cooked leather, which was all he had left of a goat he had stolen.

The Derwish ate, was satisfied, and spoke. "Thrice greater than normal dates are the fruits of your neighbor. . . . How big do you want yours to be, O Hassan, son of I-don't-know-who?"

Hassan thought for a moment and said, "Allah give

you children and cattle! I wish my dates were three times bigger than you can make them."

"Very well," said the Derwish. "Here is a bird which I brought with me from the Far East. Tell him that each of your dates has become as big as three of your dates."

"I wish you women and camels, O Derwish—who smell as pleasant as olives—but what is the use of telling this bird that which is not?"

"Do as I tell you," resumed the wise man. "That is why I am a Derwish, so you cannot understand me."

Hassan wished the bird length of feathers and called him Roc.* But it was not a Roc. It was a little bird that looked a little like a raven, with a loose tongue and a hopping way of walking. The Derwish had brought it along from Indaloes, where it had been taken by merchants who had come across the ocean from a country whose people looked like Africans, though it was far from Africa.

The reason Hassan called the beast Roc was that he had noticed that when you ask a person for something he swells up. The other way around too. He who needs something from somebody else grovels. That's the way it was in Damascus.

Hassan grovelled and said, "I am your slave, O bird Roc! My father was a dog . . . and each of my dates is as big as three of my dates!"

"That's good," said the Derwish. "Keep on going like that, and fear Allah."

* The bird Roc is a legendary creature in Eastern lore, described as being of enormous size and strength. In the *Arabian Nights,* Roc saves Sindbad the Sailor.

And Hassan did go on like that. He feared Allah
and kept on telling the bird that his dates were impos-
sibly big.

The reward of virtue was not long in coming. The
Caliph had killed his entire harem only three times,
no mother had had time yet to properly prepare her
daughters for the market of Fame, nor had Hassan met
a single little lost goat to keep him company and alive
on his mat, when, behold the bird cried, "My father is
a dog . . . ."

That wasn't necessary, but he repeated after Hassan.
"My father is a dog, get length of feathers, the dates of
Hassan, Ben . . . ."

I don't know the name of Hassan's father, and if the
man was a dog, he doesn't matter anyway.

"Hassan's dates are three times bigger than they are!"

There were rogues in Damascus who denied that.
But it didn't last long. For there was something in the
voice of the bird that made the air tremble in a way that
influenced refraction. The dates grew and grew . . . in
front of everybody's eyes. . . . And the bird kept on
shouting, "Hassan's dates are three times bigger than
they are!"

And they grew. . . . People got lockjaw from try-
ing to bite into them.

And Aöuled became very thin. But Hassan bought
many goats and kids, and he built a roof over his mat.
He became very honest and thought it a shame when
someone who didn't have kids himself ate one of his.
And he kept on fearing Allah.

He had to thank a little bird for all that wealth and
piety, a little bird that always said the same thing and
turned a lie into a truth by repeating it. Everybody

thought that Hassan's dates were big, everybody was forced to buy them, everybody. . . .

Except Hassan himself, who sustained himself secretly on Aöuled's wares. He was his only customer.

And so it has remained to this very day.

First Fairy Tale

[from *Minnebrieven*]

A self-satisfied, neatly dressed gentleman with a gold watchchain was strolling along one of the canals in Amsterdam. He was in town on "business." In a moment you'll see what business. Ahead of him walked a lady with her child. I don't know how it happened, but the child fell into the water. The mother screamed . . . and jumping in after the child, saved it.

The businessman, witnessing everything, got out his notebook and prepared to write something in it.

"Madam, may I be permitted to ask your name and address?"

"My child, my child, I've got my child back."

"Very good. May I be permitted . . ."

"I've got my child back," repeated the stubborn mother, who did not understand how anyone could ask her about anything else but her child.

"You can't get anywhere with such a woman," muttered the curious interrogator. "Pray, friend, I'll reward you handsomely if you get me the name and address of that lady by tomorrow."

Apparently the stranger got the information he

wanted, because the next day he had himself announced to the happy mother.

"Madam, I had the honor to be present . . ."

"Oh, you were there, Sir. Did you see it? I saw nothing, I heard nothing, I jumped . . ."

"Excuse me, madam, I have heard . . ."

"Heard?"

"Yes, madam, I have heard how you . . ."

"Heard? But what?"

"I have heard how you *screamed,* madam. I've come to offer you a contract with the theater."

Poor mother!

The man was a manager looking for actors. His name was PUBLIC.

[from *Minnebrieven*]

He who presents self-abasement as a virtue is a fraud.

[from *Minnebrieven*]

Writing is making an imprint of one's soul.

[from *Minnebrieven*]

The extermination of a single prejudice is worth more than the invention of ten new systems.

[from *Minnebrieven*]

No disasters are so easily borne as those of one's neighbor.

[from *Minnebrieven*]

The calling of man is to be human.

[from *Over specialiteiten*]

He who does not bother with the correct usage of a word shows unconcern for the purity of his thoughts and consequently doesn't care very much about distinguishing between good and evil.

[from *Over specialiteiten*]

Where excellence is lacking, the ordinary acts as the master; as long as available space is occupied by a soldier there is no room for generals.

[from *Vorstenschool*]

He who does not give more than he received is . . . zero, and his birth was a pointless labor.

Dionysus

[from *Over vryen arbeid,* II]

A certain country was in a state of upheaval, unrest, discord . . . agitation. Conflicts profoundly disturbed every possible "first principle." Fathers hated and disowned their sons. Women left their husbands, shopkeepers their stores and money . . . no, the discord did not go quite that far, though it went far enough.

Since such agitation was detrimental to the normal course of business—as is always the case—seventy wise men were appointed—septuagint, an ominous number! —seventy wise men with white hair and overflowing with self-esteem, to clarify the problems that agitated the people so much.

These wise men thought deeply and said a great deal. They said a great deal and sometimes thought very deeply. Some of them said a great deal without thinking quite so deeply. And then there were those who spoke without thinking at all.

And among those who spoke there were several who were understood from time to time.

But among the speakers who were understood not one was really comprehended.

I won't go into the question of whether they didn't *want* to be comprehended, that is, whether the people of this particular country applied themselves to *money-making*.

But what is certain is that the people, after much discord and much talking, remained as wise as before.

Fathers kept on disinheriting their sons. Women kept on leaving their husbands. Shopkeepers . . . no, the agitation did not go quite that far, though it kept on going far enough.

And the wise men's hair became whiter and whiter. And their self-esteem kept on growing. And they spoke . . . and spoke. . . .

But the agitation continued. The people did not become wiser. The fathers . . . you know the rest.

The dignity of the septuagint rose to high seriousness.

Their seriousness became solemn.

The solemnity reached for pathos.

The people were touched by it. But only because of the unpleasant realization which one calls agitation, and not at all from the more desirable emotion of gratitude for light received in darkness.

And the fathers . . . yes, you know that already.

Being detestably irresponsible I neglected to mention what constituted the difference. I will tell you. The question which agitated the people, which disinherited sons, which drove the women away from their men, which the shopkeepers . . . no, not the shopkeepers. The question which so preoccupied the septuagint— while preserving their self-esteem—that question was the following: "Did the holy Dionysus, after his death, walk with his head under his right or under his left arm?"

Then there came a simple man who did not have white hair and did not have self-esteem at all, from which, keeping an eye on all that other esteem, one could conclude . . . well, that doesn't matter. He said to the people: "Dear people, Dionysus did *not* walk after his death. He did *not* take his head under his arm, neither under the left nor under the right arm."

The people threw filth at the man. That's a matter of course. The disinherited sons threw along with the others. They especially shouldn't have done that. And behold, the temptation to throw filth was too strong even for the shopkeepers. This time they left their shops and money for a moment.

But the man who did not have self-esteem and did not have white hair thought of a means to put an end to the pointless agitation of the people and to the equally

pointless—misunderstood and not comprehended—
dignity of the septuagint. He took a chair, stood on top
of it, and said: "Listen citizens, listen to the word which
is spoken to you about, nay, through the holy Dionysus.
He appeared to me in a dream and asked me to greet
you all. He thanks you for your diligence in the right-
left-question. But the goodly Saint does not want you
to go too far in your passionate striving for the truth,
lest you become victims of your quenchless thirst for
righteousness. Therefore, O noble fathers, disinherited
sons, runaway wives, and so on, listen to what the holy
man has told me and immediately put an end to your
agitation.

"After his beheading, to prevent rivalry between his
two arms the peerless Dionysus took his body between
his teeth and in that manner went forth!"

The people cheered. The speaker was hung with
laurels. Everybody was content. Everybody . . . except the Septuagint who had lost a little of their weight,
of their respect and their self-esteem. . . .

[from a note added by Multatuli to *Idee* 165]

Lukewarm believers do not risk the exhaustion of
doubt; it is possible to create the courage to doubt God's
existence only from a very high degree of profound
faith.

[from a note added by Multatuli to *Idee* 186]

Jesus was thrice crucified. Once by the Jews, then by
his biographers, and finally by the Christians them-

selves. He never had more malicious enemies than the last of these.

[from *Japanse gesprekken*]

Faith is the voluntary incarceration of the mind.

[from *Pruisen en Nederland*]

Even the richest merchant is humble with a customer when he thinks he can earn a penny.

[from *Causerieën*]

Is there anything smaller, more insignificant, than mediocrity? A dwarf will always be more interesting than a little man 4½ feet tall, and from a philosophical point of view a lunatic is more noteworthy than a blockhead. Small men produce small ideas and with these they lead small people to a small goal.

[from *Causerieën*]

When Bonaparte left for Egypt, he advised his officers to study history. It is a great pity that our politicians have hardly any chance to make a trip to Egypt in the company of a genius.

Selections from the *Ideeën*

[1]

Perhaps nothing is entirely true, not even this.

[2]

Two left-handed gloves do not make a pair. Two half truths do not make a truth.

[8]

The decision to do something great can be made either with calm determination or with enthusiasm. The first way is naturally superior. This kind of superiority, however, is seldom found, except now and then in a rare individual. With committees, *never*.

The grandiose resolutions of a committee are always made in a fit of passion amid a great deal of shouting. All of which is called, pretentiously, "by acclaim."

I pray you, don't interpret this to mean that a committee which yells and loses its temper makes great resolutions.

[13]

It is very difficult to express oneself with precision. He who bemoans the lack of depth in this *idee** is not used to devoting himself to precise expression.

[15]

A Dutch mother disapproves of the French habit of having a hired woman nurse her child. I also find it horrible.

A Dutch mother is very miserable if, through weakness or illness, she is prevented from being a "complete mother," and cannot nurse the child herself. For by virtue of giving birth to it, she became, if only in part, the mother.

But fathers send their children to school.

Just as knowledge is superior to ignorance, as idea is superior to matter, as spirit is superior to body . . . so is a Dutch father inferior to a French mother.

I am not speaking of *force majeure.*

A mother who does not have nourishing milk is to be pitied.

A mother who *does* have nourishing milk and forces it back into her disappointed glands, robbing her child, is criminal.

And a father who subcontracts the humanization of

* *Idee* in Dutch means both a mental notion and its written form, the latter being synonymous with Pascal's use of *pensée.* Since Multatuli employs the word in both senses, as well as to imply *concept, mental image, notion,* the original word is maintained throughout the text.

49

his son for so much per month . . . such a father
should have married a French woman.

[30]

If a grain could speak, it would complain that there is
pain in germination.

[46]

I give suggestions, not rules.

[48]

A horseman fell off his horse, and since that time anyone who fell off his horse has called himself a horseman.

[50]

I tried on a hat and said, "It's a perfect size." My little
son needed a hat and wanted to have the same size.
    "Daddy, you said that size was good."
    What a child!

[54]

I live above a bakery.
    "I never eat those things," says the woman who
waits on me, pointing at the pastries, "because, you

understand mister, that when you make them yourself and you're always around them, and you see those things all the time and smell them all the time, then you'll know . . . isn't that so mister . . . I like to eat ham . . . but I never eat those things, you know what I mean?"

I said that I did and went upstairs. And I wrote: it's impossible for me to read novels, but I like to eat ham, just like that woman.

[57]

There is only one way to heaven: Golgatha. He who wants to reach it any other way is an infamous smuggler.

[59]

Accept one counsel: that you accept none.

[61]

He who is satisfied with his labor has a reason to be dissatisfied with his satisfaction.

[62]

It was evening. A woman stopped me.

"Can't you do anything better than selling yourself?" I said and pushed her away.

The next evening she again stood in front of me and threw my *Ideeën* in my face.

That pained me.

When I saw her again, I gave her some money and shook hands with her.

[68]

An idea which one comprehends immediately is often not worth comprehending.

[75–77]

"Why don't you come along tonight," said a friend, or words to that effect. "There's going to be a lecture on immortality. A baker is giving it. He's a real genius."

"Where does he live?"

My friend told me. I immediately went there and bought a roll. It was terrible. But in the evening I went to listen to the lecture. How good it was I don't know, because I haven't the vaguest notion of what immortality and lectures are all about. My friend said it was very good and, "Believe me, he's a real genius."

"His roll was awful. Look, I saved a bit of the soft part and it reminds me of fixing a window."

"That's possible. But the lecture was fine. Believe me, he's a genius. . . ."

"His rolls are bad."

"Believe me, he's a genius. I admit that his dough is like putty, but his lectures on immortality . . . you've got to remember that he dislikes baking but loves to talk. One is his job, the other his true calling. The first he considers a necessary but unpleasant exertion from four in the afternoon till eight in the morning, the other a pleasure he can only enjoy in his spare time. There's a lot to that man. I wish we could help him. He's not doing the right thing. . . ."

"Why doesn't he do the right thing, then?"

"Indeed, the man is . . ."

My friend, or whatever he was, proceeded to give me a lecture on would-be geniuses, and tried to persuade me to do something for that misplaced man.

I thought about it. I put the claylike soft part of the roll next to the bits of immortality which had stuck to my memory and came to the following conclusion:

If it is true that immortality is less like clay, and more nourishing than a roll—which I don't know— then that man should insist on playing musical chairs with his job and his calling. He should bake bread in his spare time and discuss immortality from four in the afternoon till eight in the morning.

[82]

It is a grievous sin to make the truth boring. This is one of my many complaints against Christians and most moralists.

[83]

A writer who has the time to explain everything has not much to write about.

[86]

A sailor had to have his leg amputated in a hospital in Amsterdam. Professor—I think it was Tilanus—performed the amputation. The man calmly smoked his pipe, clenched his teeth every so often, but had risen above the pain. Professor T. admired such strength of character and spoke about it with admiration while he was applying the bandage.

Suddenly the courageous patient yelled. The Professor had pricked him with a pin.

"How come . . . you scream like that, you who only a little while . . ."

"That's true . . . but you see professor, that pinprick wasn't part of it, didn't belong to it."

The sailor was right.

[90]

It is unfair of a circle to accuse the angle of being sharp.

[91]

I am angry with myself. I was thinking about God and about my woman. I understood something of the one and loved the other. I dreamt and felt I knew much and loved much. While loving and dreaming I walked into a restaurant where I ate green peas with bacon.

That's why I am angry with myself.

[94]

Something can only happen once. Something can be conceived, transmitted, told, described in an *infinite* number of ways. Therefore:

$$lie: truth = infinity: one$$

It is possible that something does *not* happen. It still can be invented, transmitted, described, in an infinite number of ways. Then it's even worse.

$$l: t = infinity: ZERO$$

Those relationships can give you goosepimples.

[102]

We become dependent on "isms" when God's existence has to be proven through Nature, and our concepts of God depend on a speck on the lens of a microscope, on one millimeter wrong on the scale of a thermometer or other measuring device, on iron in the vicinity of a compass, on an incorrectly calculated refraction, on poor achromatism in an ocular instrument, on . . . on . . .

Yes, on all sorts of things!

Sirius is so many miles away; hence: God is great.

That micro-organism* is giving speeches to his fel-

---

* In the text the word is literally "infusion animals," and refers to the microscopic animals which Leeuwenhoek first saw in 1676. Leeuwenhoek called them animalcules and noted that they consisted of various kinds. To preserve the general tone as well as the inclusiveness the term was translated as "micro-organisms."

low micro-organisms who understand and comprehend him; hence: God is great.

That fish has a fin which enables him to make a
volte with an angle of $1/1000000$ degrees; hence:
God is great.

All of this was discovered by Professor A, Doctor B
and Prosector C, and these three godserving nature-
men are the theologians of the day.

The next day it seems:

That Sirius is one mile further away! *God is one mile
greater.*

That the micro-organism was misunderstood:
God is misunderstood.

That that fish was less quick than one thought,
and in order to turn needed an angle with one
less zero in the fraction: *there is one zero less in
the amount of appreciation of God.*

If I really have to dream and guess and muse over what
I don't know, I'd rather stick with dreamy old-fashioned
theology. The study of nature is the best study there is,
but you don't learn to understand anything from it
. . . except Nature, that is to say, *everything!* And
precisely because God is *outside* of everything you are
incapable of learning to know him from nature.

[103]

A failed genius is not a genius. I do not speak of failure
occasioned by dying from convulsions or measles.

He who believes himself to be a genius will not become a genius because of that belief when he simply

56

isn't one. But if he indeed is one, and all of you say that he is *not,* then you will be right until he *forces* you to acknowledge that he is.

[107]

I will tell you how humility came into the world.

Pygmee was small of stature and liked to look over the heads of others. Which seldom happened because he was so terribly small.

He began to travel in order to find people who were smaller than he, but he didn't find them. And his desire to look over the heads of others became stronger and stronger.

He came to Patagonia where people are so big that a child, immediately after birth, can look over the head of his father.

Pygmee did not like this . . . in someone else. But since he despaired of ever finding people who were smaller than he, he thought of a remedy. He invented a virtue which legislated as its first principle: whoever is bigger than Pygmee has to bend down until he is beneath Pygmee's line of vision, and the fad gained favor. All the Patagonians became virtuous. If someone, by walking straight, sinned against the first principle of Pygmee's virtue, he was punished in a peculiar manner. All who were bent and virtuous jumped around the neck of the obstinate one, and pulled him down until his head had reached the level of Patagonian virtuousness. And whoever carried all of Patagonia on his shoulders without becoming virtuous was displayed with a sign that had a Patagonian word written on it which really meant: This man was in Pygmee's way.

This word is usually translated as *pride*.

[114]

Each virtue has illegitimate sisters who disgrace the family.

[122]

An old gentleman was reading the newspaper and held it at a distance.

"Why are you doing that?" I asked.

"Since I've become old I don't see so well up close anymore."

I wish my readers would grow old and read me at a distance.

[123]

"I don't understand *idee* X."

"Did you read them *all!*"

"No."

"Then you are not *able* to understand X."

[137]

If you like curiosities I can recommend the following. Did you ever see a dog with a hump? I never did.

Well, we definitely should be able to get one of them. Take a litter of puppies who have the misfortune of being well shaped. Say the following conjuration: "Nature, nature, nature, how stupid you are, nature!"

After that put corsets on your little dogs, preferably somewhat stiff and tight, and just watch very carefully how Nature will soon obey your spell, and will give you something crooked where, before your conjuration, she thought she was able to make do with things that were perfectly shaped.

[143]

Finding the truth—i.e., approaching the truth—would not be so difficult if we were less cowardly. In many cases we do not *dare* to know what is true.

[148]

Nature works by assembling and by its *opposite.* The latter is called, in the nature of things, to grow old, to wear out, to languish, to perish. When we talk about things which concern our nature, we call it, to die. It's always the same.

But all of this comes down to *rotting,* a word that bothers us because we are small. It's a beautiful language that sums up wearing, perishing, dying, rotting, in one word; decomposition. That word indicates so perfectly what I called the "opposite" of "assembling" in the first sentence of this Idee, that I really begin to believe our Sanskrit ancestors held doctorates in physics. A certain measure of knowledge is necessary—regarding the general situation of society for four, six or ten thousand years, a very large measure of knowledge—in order to understand that a revolting, rotten object which affects our senses in the most unpleasant fashion, contains really *nothing that is spoiled,* that only its parts were separated, that cohesion had ceased, that—to use a very simple image—the house had been torn down while conserving the materials.

No matter how simple this truth seems to contemporary scientists, I maintain that the People are still not at the same level as the society which invented the word *decomposition* and used it, that is to say, *understood* it. Really, we have gone backwards, and the legend of the bodily-resurrection doctrine has done little good!

[149]

I stated: "He who fears rotting is an enemy of life." True! And he who laments error is an enemy of truth. But I speak of *the* rotting, *the* error. Physical life is a battle against *all* rotting. Moral and spiritual life is a battle against *all* error.

It would indeed be curious if people took my ideeën concerning the necessity of error and decomposition to mean that I advocate lying and that I would just as soon see a corpse as a girl. They're capable of it.

[151]

Come on Mr. A, B, or C, be honest, do you think it's worth the trouble for a Creator, for Nature, for whatever . . . was good enough to call you into being, also to preserve you eternally?

Didn't you ever make something that later on bored you, that stood in your way, that occupied a space which could be put to better use?

[152]

If the earth is a training-school for heaven, then I deeply regret that my unknown guardian did not place me in another institution.

[155]

Seen from the moon we are all the same size.

[157]

Immortality without eternity is a rope with only one end.

[158]

I want to say something about humor, and what belongs to it. All definitions are difficult. Imagine that moonpeople, who have no body below their waists, no legs and no feet—because moonpeople don't exist—

imagine that such a moonperson, who, as a result of lacking such things—perhaps also from lack of existence—had never seen a chair and asked you, what, among you earthlings, is a chair? *I* wouldn't be able to explain it to him. Or, if he were satisfied with my explanation, it would only prove that he had little notion of such "concepts" as chairs.

Yet I can tell you—practically anytime—what humor is. *Humor is the depiction of Nature,* and nothing else. This is perfectly simple. But if it were complicated it would, *primo,* not be true, and *secundo,* I wouldn't have had to tell you, since complicated truths are generally known.

Humor is the depiction of Nature. Nature itself is very humorous. Yes, it *alone* is humorous. Indeed, it is *always* humorous. I will show that in a moment. What we call humor is merely a copy of it.

Such a depiction of Nature can be done in a variety of ways. It can be done with sounds, colors, forms, tin, sign, gesture; in short we can counterfeit Nature in as many ways as we have means of communicating an impression.

But of what consists the humor of Nature? In its *stupidity* as related to its generality.

Its stupidity. Nature is just as stupid as any other tool which, according to fixed measures, according to certain —no, according to *given*—forces, chops, cuts, stamps, presses, lifts, turns, grinds, assembles, pulverizes. You say that such a tool is beautiful? That is to say, it remains a tool, nothing more. It is a tool that works, or more precisely, which is forced by certain pressures to move itself in a manner necessary to achieve a goal which lies totally outside the consciousness of the tool

62

itself. It might be correct to say: the watch is *being* run.

In a rolling mill you see, among other applications of steam power, a big pair of scissors that constantly yawns and bites. If you don't stick anything between it, it cuts the air. But its proper purpose is to cut through plates of copper, which is what it does faithfully without giving the slightest indication that it understands the difference between those plates and the air. Give the pair of scissors a little piece of paper, it will cut it. A book, it will cut it. You can't tell by the looks of it whether it could distinguish between a tough sermon and an incoherent speech.

Go even further. You're paying a visit to that rolling mill with some ladies. The scissors cut . . . cut . . .

That girl next to you is eighteen years old. She is sweet, comely, you could encircle her waist.

Grab her neck between thumb and finger of the left hand, grab her ankles with your right hand, hold her horizontally, stretch her forward, bring that middle you found so sweet . . .

The scissors cut . . . cut air, during the time you need to pick up that sweet child.

Bring her—but carefully, because if you touch the scissors you might hurt yourself—bring her at the moment when the two blades have formed the largest possible angle, when the scissors yawn . . .

Wait a minute . . . this time it is too late. . . . It closes already and once more cuts air which isn't bothered by the cutting at all. . . .

Now is the time . . . now . . . exactly . . . you've got it!

The girl has been cut in two. You hold a half in each hand, and the scissors has already cut air five times with the same indifference before you have time to bring those two halves back together again, and with the halved child you stand there wondering about the mechanical stupidity of those scissors which don't know what they cut. Nature is as stupid as those scissors.

Nature is general. We saw its stupidity in the rolling mill. To make you aware of the generality of Nature I invite you to visit a shop, or better, a *toko* in Batavia.*
For those people who do not know the Indies, I'll just mention that a *toko* is to a shop as everything is to nothing.

In a store things are sold, certain kinds of goods. In a *toko* all kinds of things are sold, all goods, *everything.* Just ask for shoe polish, ham, toothpaste, almanacs, pictures of ministers, *bonshommes,* tumblers, skates, mourning bands, shares in a ship or buckles for breeches . . . all of this is supplied by a true *toko.*

Nature is such a *toko.* In its infinite storeroom it has *everything!* Air, sea, life, love, weight, illness, joy, beauty, character, pain, sound, haste, slowness, strength, growth, decomposition, death. It doesn't matter here if it brings all of this about by one single means, *movement,* just as it is irrelevant to us whether the shop received its wares from one single factory. Enough, the wares are there.

But in the large store of Nature everything is all over the place. The buffoon sits astride the neck of the little bronze woman who weeps for her child. A plaster-of-paris Napoleon stands between two decks of cards, and

* Batavia was the Dutch name for what was once the capital of the Dutch East Indies, now Djakarta, the capital of Indonesia.

64

a bottle of cognac is wrapped in a pamphlet from tee-totallers.

Because Nature is *stupid*. It has no notion of *display*. That is why it is humorous and he who copies it well is humorous also.

[160]

I once lived near a mountain that gave off smoke. When I saw it for the first time, I thought—corrupted by schoolbooks—that such a mountain afforded a beautiful sight. I remembered that I should be in rapture and did what I held to be my duty. Upon rising in the morning I saw that mountain and what it blew out. Half an hour later I saw it again, with its smoke. A little later, the same thing. The following day, the same. Weeks, months, one after the other . . . for two long years, every day, every hour, every moment, I saw the same thing. The mountain stood there and blew smoke.

But *I* lived. I thought. I pondered, experienced, suffered, strove and fought. . . .

My mountain blew smoke.

I suffered . . . *it* blew. The thing couldn't do anything but that. If I spoke of faith, it gave off smoke. Of happiness, smoke. Of the future, smoke. Of glory, smoke. Of fidelity, love, sacrifice, soul, bliss, poetry, eternity and God—it always gave off smoke, smoke, nothing but smoke. The thing had nothing else, knew nothing else, understood nothing else. . . .

That stupid buffoon was always sitting on my neck as if that were its proper place.

[173]

It's childish—that is to say, *human*—always to spar
with solar systems to prove something about a personal
god. Make the water in your basin go around. Watch
the floating soap bubbles gather together, and you see
a miniature solar system. Every little sphere takes its
given place according to the forces in the field. The
earth, the sun, Sirius, do the same. But think the rim of
the bowl away. For space is infinite, as matter is eternal.

[175]

There is only one mystery: being. The rest follows from
the characteristics of being. And yet that mystery is not
so profound as the opposite would be. Just think about
the absurdity of: non-being.

[181]

What have you done to the world, O Christians? I
avert my eyes from your disgusting History which you
have falsified and messed up, *to the greater glory of
God.* You call Constantine *great,** and whatever else
you say is just as true as that. I avert my eyes from your
History, to contemplate something you cannot distort,
can *not* churchify—your families, your daughters.
What have you done to them? What have you done to
woman?

* Constantine the Great (A.D. 274–337), Roman emperor
who reunited the empire and established Constantinople. He
was a champion of the Christian church, but—and perhaps
this is the reason for Multatuli's cynicism—it could be said
that he needed the religion for political purposes.

To maintain the rights you obtained by force, you daily make your women household tools, or worse, and your daughters Kaspar Hausers or Javanese.* You treat your women even worse than your Bible decrees, but not everything concerning their degraded position can be blamed on Mosaic or apostolic stipulations. Nowhere do I read: "Keep your wife stupid," or, "Beware lest your daughters acquire an appetite for science." Once such submissiveness has been accepted, the rest follows inevitably. As long as slavery exists in South America, the slaveholders will quite naturally forbid their slaves to read. At the same time the commandment to be submissive legalizes only those actions by which it can maintain itself.

Indeed, it is written: women are to be *submissive*. Up to what point? Where do you draw the line? That isn't spelled out. There is no mention of a limit. The apostle leaves it to your discretion, gentlemen.

And even if that were not the case, take a good look at them, those lords of creation, men! Follow them in their niceties, in their puny striving, their narrow-mindedness, their ignorance, their cowardice, and ask yourself whether it is proper and just that the *other* half of the human race so readily has to be submissive to *that* half?

The very demands that men make reveal that their

* Kaspar Hauser was a mysterious figure who appeared in the town of Nüremberg one day, uneducated and incapable of recognizing objects. He became the center of a controversy in Germany caused by a modish interest in the occult. He died in 1833 from a wound which, he maintained, had been inflicted on him by a strange figure.

The Javanese are here referred to as the oppressed people of Dutch colonialism (see the Introduction).

claim is unfounded. To be lord in the domain of morality, one must first understand justice, and it is unjust to place woman, as such, beneath man. Imagine *Cornelia, Sappho, Charlotte Corday, Madame de Staël, Harriet Beecher Stowe,* * *beneath* the first punk that comes along!

But who should rule, then? The answer is very simple: there are to be no rulers.

"Fine! But who should have the most influence?"

"Well . . . whoever deserves it."

"Fine again but . . . who deserves it?"

"Whoever is the most developed as a *human being*. The genitals have as little to do with this as does the color of hair."

"But . . . if he or she who is the most developed as a human being fails to obtain the influence which rightfully belongs to him or her?"

Then I doubt the superior development of such a person and seriously recommend further development. Biblical regulations about the treatment of woman, her

---

* Cornelia was mother of the Roman leaders Tiberius and Gaius Gracchus (2nd century B.C.). Tradition made her the model of Roman motherhood.

Charlotte Corday (1768–93) was the French revolutionary who killed Marat in his bath.

Madame de Staël (1766–1817) was the chief exponent of French Romanticism during its initial stage. Unhappily married, she had many love affairs with famous men of her day, and finally found happiness by marrying an officer who was considerably younger. Because of her writings and political activities Napoleon distrusted her and exiled her twice.

Harriet Beecher Stowe (1811–96) was the author of *Uncle Tom's Cabin* (1853); Multatuli felt an intellectual kinship with her because of this book and her subsequent defense of it, *A Key to Uncle Tom's Cabin* (1853).

place in society, are of such a nature that, for decency's sake, I cannot copy them out in my *Ideeën.*

Woman is given away, sold, exchanged, loaned out like a cow. Indeed, she is *below* the cow. She is cut up quite casually and the pieces of her body are used as convocation letters or announcement cards.* And as we have seen, Jesus places her even lower, he *ignores* woman.† He found a way to discuss marriage without even mentioning her. Marriage—you would think a woman necessary for that, even though she is excluded *everywhere* else!

But I'll forget about regulations and the law, and speak about mores and their use. I no longer say: *Christians!* what have you done to woman? Now I ask: Man, what have *you* done to her?

* Chapter 19 of the Book of Judges contains the story of a man who, while travelling with his wife, stays overnight in a town where a man invites them to his house. That night a group of local citizens surround the house with the intent of committing violence. In answer to this threat the host and his guest offer the traveller's wife in order to appease the attackers. The woman is raped to death. When the husband has returned home with the body of his wife, he cuts her up into twelve pieces and sends these around the country as tokens of his anger.
† Multatuli's reference to Christ's inhumanity to women seems impossible to corroborate. In fact, Christ's own words in the New Testament would indicate quite the opposite. Perhaps Multatuli had St. Paul in mind.

Inhabitants of a country cannot be said to be either free or not free because of their laws. The measure of their freedom is determined by their mores.

Which law orders you to neglect the education of your daughters? And which one says you should make your women unsalaried housekeepers? Morality does that.

Which law prescribes that you should send your children to school and farm their education out for quarterly rent? Morality does that.

Where is the law that forces you to let your brood be chloroformed by Reverend Splithair? Morality does that.

Where is it written that you are forbidden to give your family *pleasure?* Where is it ordered that you should plague it with churchgoing, sermonizing, catechism and the practice of all sorts of other things which your family doesn't need because they don't exist? Morality does that.

Where is it written that you have to force a "faith" on your loved one which you yourself gave up long ago? Morality does that.

Where is it decreed that your wife doesn't have a voice in the concerns of your house—which are *her* concerns, too, after all—and in those of *her* children? Morality does that.

Where is it dictated that you should show your daughter the door when she shows you a child which is the fruit of love, of surprise . . . yes, even when it is the fruit of lust and frivolity? Morality does that.

Finally, where is it indicated that a lukewarm, cowardly: *"That's the custom!"* is a lawful excuse for violating the highest, the only, holy laws of common sense? Morality does that.

[195]

Morality: the things you do to our daughters! You force them to lie and dissemble. They are not allowed to know what they know, feel what they feel, desire what they desire, be what they are.

"A girl doesn't do things like that. A girl doesn't say things like that. A girl doesn't ask things like that. A girl doesn't talk like that!" That is the order of the day in bringing up a girl. And if such a poor, protected child believes, acquieses, obeys . . . if she has spent her sweet blossoming time quite submissively being pruned and trimmed, her desire, spirit and emotions stifled and raped . . . when she has become nicely distorted, crushed, ruined, remained a good girl—that's what morality calls good!—then she has a chance to have some clod offer her the reward for so much goodness by appointing her supervisor of his linen closet and by making her the exclusive licensing-machine to keep his honorable lineage going. It's really worth it!

[208]

Once upon a time it really happened, according to the newspapers, that in Detmold, not far from Frankfurt, a man cut his son's throat. He had stacked some wood and was busily dragging the corpse towards it when he saw a ram, with its horns entangled in the thicket. You really believe that?

No, there was no ram. But the "Lord" sent a few neighbors who took the corpse away from him. These stupid neighbors thought that it was wrong to burn up one's children.

"He wanted to offer the Lord his first born," said the man. . . . And, O shame, O curse, O godforsaken, godless brutality of the Detmold police . . . they arrested that man.

Just imagine, Abraham at Moria, bound like a criminal and brought before a judge for sentencing!

And the Lord just lets the police do what they want? That's impossible.

I would guess that the ram, which did not appear when this man killed his Isaac, will suddenly appear as a substitute, as soon as that pious father is treated as the murderer of his child by worldly authority. . . . Or—that's the way it is—as a madman.

But again I have to admit that I feel closer to such a madman than to lukewarm believers.

I pity that man, but I understand him.

I despise the wretches who drove him crazy with their pious blabbering without—mark it well!—ever cutting the throat of their own children. As soon as I hear a minister preach again about "Aaabraham, the faaather of the faithful, an exaaample for true belieeevers" I will say: "You first please . . . after you, if you don't mind!"

Not so long ago such an Abraham sacrifice was also offered in Antwerp. That father of the faithful is now locked up. I wonder whether we will ever be able to count his descendants like the sand which is upon the seashore.*

[209]

A few days ago a young girl, well behaved, pious, and domesticated, was taken by her family to an insane asylum in Utrecht.

The lady who was in charge of female patients in that asylum said to the family, "Our regulations are simple. Gentleness is the main thing. Furthermore, as a matter of course, light, air, distraction, exercise, proper recreation . . ."

When they were leaving, the members of the poor patient's family discussed these regulations, and a younger sister asked the father, "Light, air, distraction . . . exercise . . . proper recreation. . . . Father, what if we had provided that *before* our poor sister became crazy?"

I don't know what the father answered.

But *I* will say: it would have been better if someone had put a stone around his neck . . . and everything else that goes with it, a second before his marriage, than for him to have to hear such a question from the mouth of his child . . . than to have to *deserve* such a question from his child.

And there are many fathers like that, for whom I advise either a stone, or some obedience to Jesus' hint in Matthew 19.†

* The story of Abraham and Isaac is in Gen. 22:17.
† Multatuli refers to the suggestion that there are people who simply shouldn't get married (Matt. 19:10–12).

It is not true that a child owes his parents submission
and love. That miserable rule was invented for the convenience of parents who felt their lack of spiritual superiority and who were too lazy or too dry of heart to
merit love.

To my children. You are still a little too young to understand me. But the time will come when you will read
what I am saying here. If ever, in your presence, I in-
voke my fatherhood . . . laugh at me!

If I ever legislate submission to you . . . mock me!

If I ever demand love from you . . . because . . .
because . . . how shall I put it?

Love from you, because something once happened,
and I wasn't even thinking of *you* at the time at all.
Love, because I did something before you even existed.
Love because . . . fill it in, children. You can do it
when you are able to read what your father is writing,
fill it all in.

If I ever demanded love, just because . . . throw
filth at me!

Laugh at me, mock me, throw filth at me, if I ever
demand submission or love . . . *just because!*

Imagine that the commandment to honor your father
and mother was botched by translators. Yes, yes, that's
it. Believe me, it says, "Hate your father, that you may
live long!"

Try it sometime!

I would like to see a "Lord" who had the power to

stop you from loving your mother, even if he promised you ten long lives, in ten countries at once. With or without the commandment, for or against the commandment, with or without decrees, she and I will be able to earn your love through love.

And if we can't do that then we can lay no claim to love.

Your *submissiveness* will exist as long, and only as long, as my mind is better than yours, because I began many years earlier. That span of time you will soon overtake, especially since I so often stand still on my path, alas! Children, you will have nothing to thank me for except for what I did *after* your birth, and not even for that. Love finds its rewards in itself. Oh, how I wish you were already able to read my *Ideeën,* and everything I am saving for all of you. Oh, I can hear it already:

"We do love you, father, but you don't need to be our *father* for that!"

[213]

It is strange that so many people are so presumptuous as to have children. I know a zoo keeper who knows how to handle tigers. Another one is just right for the birds. Even artificial fish-breeding has its specialists. But everybody keeps children.

[220]

The highest measure of courage is pride.

[221]

He who speaks humbly of himself becomes angry if you believe him and furious if you repeat what he says.

[226]

I would like to meet myself some time, to know how I would like myself. But I'd have to be in an extremely good state of mind on such a day, because I don't like unpleasantness.

[235]

He who has never fallen does not understand exactly what is required to stand firm.

[251]

A professor of ichthyology was giving a lecture. The students were listening . . . well, the way students usually listen, not to mention students of ichthyology!

"The carp, gentlemen, the carp . . ."

Which was followed by something about carps. . . .

"The carp, gentlemen . . .

And behold, a carp came swimming into the lecture room. How the beast made it, considering how dry the place was, does not concern us. The poor students had suffered from that condition for such a long time already—and a carp is no better than a student.

"There he is," they shouted with one voice.

And they left the professor standing there with his discourse *about* the carp, and went to go *look* at the carp.

I think that this is all very normal and proper on the part of the students. But I wish that we would do the same, and apply ourselves more to contemplating mankind—and women too, you men—than to listening to lecture notes *about* people.

[252]

There is not a single person whose emotional history is not more important than the longest, most beautifully made novel.

[254]

Slanderers and poets do not create. They arrange.

[261]

A butterfly floated high, high up in the air. She was enjoying her beauty and freedom, and she delighted especially in perceiving everything that was beneath her.

"Come, come up here . . . up high!" she seemed to be calling to her sisters, who, far below her, fluttered around the flowers of the earth.

"We are sipping honey, and staying down here."

"O dear sisters, if you only knew how wonderful it is to be able to oversee everything. . . . Come, up here, why don't you come?"

"Are there flowers up there we can suck honey from, the honey we butterflies need to live?"

"From up here you can *see* all the flowers . . . and it is such a pleasure. . . ."

"Do you have honey up there?"

It's true, there was no honey up there!

The poor butterfly who disliked living below became weary. . . .

But she still tried to keep herself up! It was so wonderful, she thought, to be able to oversee everything, to understand everything with one glance.

But honey. . . . Honey? No, there was no honey up there.

And she became weak, the poor butterfly. Her wing-stroke became slower and slower.

And she sank . . . and already she could oversee less.

And yet she wanted . . .

No, it was no use . . . she descended. . . .

"Look, there she comes," called the sisters. "What did we tell you? You do come to suck honey, just like us, from the flowers down here. We knew it!"

So the sisters called, happy because they were right, although they were right because they were ignorant of the beauty up above.

"Come and suck honey like us!"

And the butterfly descended . . . lower . . . and wanted still . . .

There was a flowering bush . . . would she be able to reach it?

She no longer descended . . . would she be able to reach it?

She no longer descended . . . she was falling! She fell next to the bush, on the road, in the track. . . .

She was trampled there by a donkey.

[263]

There is nothing more poetic than the truth. He who does not see poetry in that will always remain a meager versifier outside of it.

[283]

.   .   .   .

[284]

The previous number contains several hundred Ideeën which I didn't write down because misery prevented me from doing so.

Is this an Idee?

Yes and no.

Not now, but years from now, it will give food for Ideeën to those who will write the history of our times.

It's a pity that the most fitting title for such a history has already been swiped by Victor Hugo, who made it into a shingle for a novel.

[302]

There is no honor to be won from adversaries who have no character.

[303]

Principles are things which one calls upon to avoid something unpleasant.

[310]

Socrates was a conceited fool, and the Athenians were quite right to condemn him. It's just that I find his punishment somewhat light. To die! After all, everyone is going to do that, even the most innocent! I think it is very unfair that someone who dedicated himself to the public good was given as a *punishment* something that, in the final analysis, is experienced by the most sober nincompoop who ever represented a people. The Athenians were too hot-tempered, just like the Jews.

But Socrates! See what I find about him in Plutarch:

"It was a custom in Athens that the accused were to defend themselves before the tribunal with skillful speeches, and to try to work on the emotions of their judges through tears and pleas. Socrates considered it beneath him to use such unworthy means. . . ."

I already told you that Socrates was crazy.

"In his simple plea he made reference to the course of his life. . . ."

Again, very stupid. He seemed to think that they would pay attention to what he had *done.* That wasn't the question, O Socrates! You should have said, "I am a liberal . . . or a conservative," depending on which way the wind was blowing. You should have spoken of your faith—old-fashioned or modern, again, depending on the way it would come out. You should have said something about principles and doctrines, at least according to the fads of the day. You see, that was your mistake! Plutarch was right to call your defense simple, and true, to the point of imbecility.

All right, so Socrates pointed to the course of his life. But:

"This defense did not find favor with his judges, and they condemned him to death. . . ."

There again you have that damned indolence of the Athenians who appeared to have no notion of Christian torture, those stupid heathens!

"According to Athenian custom the condemned man himself had to declare what kind of punishment he thought he deserved. This was asked of Socrates too, who declared that he believed he deserved to be supported at public expense by the state, as if he were a winner in the Olympic games."

Wasn't I right when I said that Socrates was crazy? Not a trace of Christian humility! But . . . yes, of course:

"By this answer he embittered his judges even more. . . ." I believe it. Because it is very unpleasant, when you think you have just condemned somebody, that such a person should dare to lay claim to a reward. The judges were absolutely right to be bitter about such an answer, and,

"Many of them who had first voted against the penalty of death now voted for it. He was condemned."

Thus far Plutarch. That dry recorder of lives doesn't even give a single word of praise for those embittered judges.

I think that Plutarch was a liberal and that the judges were conservative, or vice versa, since in Greece one never praised anybody who belonged to another party.

[324]

The most intense expression of grief is sarcasm.

[326]

There is not a single individual who would not be accused of being a criminal if he permitted himself what the state permits itself.

[336]

I create an individual in the following manner: I gather the properties of many people, add them up and divide them by the number of people. I think of a story about that individual: "Adventures of Mediocrity or The Life and Deeds of an Averaged Man."

It was born at several times, in several voting districts. It attended all sorts of institutions with praise and profit where mediocrity was taught, and it was never *homogeneously* convicted for theft or murder. It married many ladies and produced averages of . . . everything. It baked bread and political science. It brewed beer and strife. It distilled gin and suspicion. It made vats and intrigues. It sold coffee and religion, wisdom, syrup and "first" principles.*

It walked three steps forward—and three steps backward—and remained where it was. It sank and rose, and ended up neither higher nor lower. It fell ill, and died, and lived on . . . what a pity! It talked constantly, but said yes and no one right after the other, so that it seemed not to have spoken at all. It was neither blue nor yellow, nor red nor green nor grey, but all paints intermingled: a mishmash.

It was neither high nor low, neither deep nor broad nor long, not fat, not thin . . . it was no thing.

It didn't do this, it didn't do that, it did one thing and another, it did all sorts of things and consequently it did nothing. . . .

That is to say, because it had been delegated to do at least something, it did much evil.

[337]

It is a sad affair that the word "original" is an indication of praise.

[338]

I thank you, dear Nature, for decreeing that, at the very least, everybody remains responsible for his own digestion.

* Ironic reference to the Aristotelian concept of the philosophers' quest for first principles.

[339]

A legislator is not allowed to be misunderstood.

[340]

It was winter. Down there on that wide canal people were amusing themselves with skating. The ice was level with the road. All you had to do was just step out onto it.

Yet a bridge had been laid across a wide trench which I had not seen the day before. And everybody who crossed the bridge had to pay a penny to the man who had made the little bridge, "because of the trench," he said.

But some were whispering, "He made the trench because of the bridge."

Isn't it a shame that people have found a way to make the explanation of the law into a profitable *occupation?*

[341]

Society is everywhere cut through with such trenches, which, most of the time, are there simply to keep the "bridgeman" alive.

What would happen to educators if we simply wrote the way a civilized human being speaks?

What of the military, if we wanted to understand that the smallest nation is stronger than the biggest army?

What of lawyers, if we had lawmakers who were capable of expressing their thoughts clearly?

What of ministers, if we understood that each of us should look for his religion in his own heart?

And finally, what of the moralists, if we knew how to recover those mores in sweet Nature?

Goodness, all those bridgemen out of work!

[343]

Often more courage is required to tackle trivia than to combat great wrongs. Trivial things have more supporters.

[345]

Just look around you, my son, and notice how wisely Providence has created everything. That bird lays its eggs in its own nest. Its young will come out by the time there are worms and flies to feed themselves. Then they will sing a hymn of praise to honor the Creator who overwhelms His creatures with benefactions. . . .

"Do those worms sing too, daddy?"

[346]

I know a father who knows exactly how much his son's education has cost him. He writes everything down. But he does not write down what he learns from his child. That is unfair.

[347]

Two boys fell into the water. One was saved because "God is good." The other drowned. Because God is evil?

[358]

Heine thought of immortality when he saw a pair of neatly polished boots standing by a grave.

What if the undertaker's maid had put a nightcap there to bleach?

[359]

I love Heine so much that I am glad I never met him.

[368]

Little would remain of what we call conscience if we could think away the necessary results of the evil that was committed.

[393]

Doubt always has a paralyzing effect, whether or not it is relevant to the matter at hand. Furthermore, if one is disturbed while angry it is very difficult to find the exact place again where one left off.

[398]

Obviously, genius does not die; otherwise it wouldn't
be worthwhile for a genius to allow himself to be born.

[408]

There is not such a wide gap between spirit and intellect as is asserted by creatures who lack both.

[411]

It happens often that we do not see something because
it is too great.

[433]

Holy Kwip, or Kwap, was beheaded. Instead of abid-
ing by it and bearing it as you and I would have done,
reader, he took his head under his arm and walked away
with it.

For my part I doubt the possibility of that walk,
since, in order to do something, first we need to have
the will, the intention, or, at least the unconscious reason to do it. The organs which pick up that intention, or
are affected by that reason, are located in the brain, and
from there the nerves transport the order to those parts
of the body which have been charged with its execution.
At the moment when holy Kwip had the will, or found
a reason, to walk away with his head, that head was

severed from his body and as such there was a blockage
in the service route between the brain and other parts
of his body. His hand could not know that it should
place the head under the arm, the arm had not received
an order to hold on to the head, and the legs stayed de-
prived of the invitation to have Kwip walk away. Hence
I argue that that defect in communication . . .

"O thou stupid spirit of contrariness, behold thyself
caught in the bonds of worldly wisdom. What's so nice
about it is that Kwip's brain had given the order to
walk off with his head before the blockage of communication. . . ."

Don't *argue* with the pious!

[434]

"But," says the Protestant, "we don't believe those crazy
stories about Kwip or Kwap, either. We are far removed from the Catholics. We despise human inven-
tions, fables, priest-nonsense . . . just look at *our* religion! With us everything is common sense. We don't
get stuck in crazy elaborations, we hold on to the spirit
—morality, you know?—to the morality and the spirit
which has been revealed and imparted by our Lord
Jesus Christ, who was born of a virgin, died for our sins
on the cross, descended into hell, and ascended into
heaven. . . ."

"—!"

Someone visited a madhouse. He was accompanied
on his tour by a person who provided him with information about the kinds of madness the inmates were
suffering from. The guide seemed sensitive by nature,

that is to say, he showed himself deeply moved by the plight of those poor fools. One was a king, the second a pincushion, the third, fourth, fifth . . . up to the twenty-third, were poets. Then there followed the religious nuts—I didn't count them—then a couple of love nuts—not many, because there are fewer of those than one thinks—followed by those who suffered from delusions of grandeur, fame nuts, money nuts . . . in short it was the world in miniature.

"It's sure strange and sad," said the friendly guide, "that the human spirit can stray so much. That man over there imagines he is the pope, and this one here thinks he's a burning candle! And that's not right, Sir. Because you should understand that if it were true, I would have blown him out long ago."

The guide who protested against the craziness of the others thought himself to be the southwest wind. . . .

That protestant wind was the most difficult madman of the whole place.

[438]

After the death of his wife, my friend Ornis bought some birds for diversion. If I had to measure his grief over the loss of his better half according to the number of fowl that replaced her, I would have to admit that he was very sad. Because the number of his birds was great. He had finches who could see and ones that couldn't. Canary birds, black, green and yellow ones. Seventeen kinds of pigeons. Also parrots, cockatoos, thrushes, magpies, chickens, ravens, peacocks, ducks, turkeys, geese, grouse, cassowaries, ostriches and many more . . . too many to name, just like the patriotic heroes in a school-book.

How he got that collection I don't know, and it doesn't have anything to do with the story I want to tell.

One morning Ornis had to leave town. He would be absent for some time. . . .

"Dear friend," he said, "I appeal to your friendship."

I don't like such appeals. There are people who take friendship literally and who turn such appeals into a job.

"I have to leave town," he continued, "and I don't know how I am going to . . ."

"Well, buy a ticket for the train."

"No, it isn't that. I don't know what to do with my birds. . . ."

"What if you took them with you," I suggested.

"That's not possible because of the expense. Besides, Liwi is in heat. . . ." Liwi was a youthful canary who whistled "Coming Through the Rye."

"All right, then leave your birds at home."

"You can tell that you've never been married . . . that you've never kept birds. 'Leave them home' is easier said than done! Who will take care of them while I am gone? Who will talk to them, teach them to warble, give them food, clean them?"

"I see . . . so that's what it's all about! And your appeal to my friendship . . ."

"Yes, that is so. I wanted, during my absence, to charge you with the care of my birds."

"I have too many things to do."

"Postpone them. My birds . . ."

"My father is sick."

"What has that to do with it! My birds . . ."

"My children have measles."

"Keep them warm. My birds . . ."

"My business affairs are in a mess."

"Ask to extend your payments. My birds . . ."

"Dear Ornis, I don't know anything about birds."

"How . . ."

"Believe me, I have never kept birds. I really don't know how to take care of them."

"That's different. You did right to tell me that. Now I'll try to find someone to whom I can entrust my darlings."

And Ornis finally left me in peace, *because I didn't know anything* about birds.

Now I wonder what it is that moves so many people to keep children?

[447]

In Samojedia—I don't know whether that is actually the name of the country, but that's a gap in the language which we will have to fill—it's the custom in Samojedia to smear yourself all over with rancid train oil. A young Samojed neglected to do this. He didn't smear himself at all, neither with train oil nor with anything else.

"You do not follow our mores," said a Samojedian philosopher. . . . You don't *have* any morals . . . you are *a*moral."

That was very well put.

The young amoral Samojed was abused, of course. He caught more seals than anyone else, but to no avail.

They took his seals away from him, gave them to trained Samojeds, and they let him starve.

But it became even worse.

After having lived for some time in an unsmeared state, the young Samojed finally began to wash himself with Eau de Cologne. . . .

Nobody could stand this redolence in Samojedia!

"He acts *against* our mores," said the philosopher of the day, "He is *im*moral! Come, let us continue robbing him of the seals he has caught and furthermore beat . . ."

They did so.

But since Samojedia did not know slander, copyright, insinuation, stupid orthodoxy, nor false liberalism, suspect politics, rotten officials, nor a corrupt government . . . they beat their patient with the gnawed bones of the seals he had caught.

[450]

There is but one evil, one crime, one sin: lack of heart.

[451]

If I have to choose between a calf and him who kneels in front of it, I choose the calf. The animal is dumb and unable to say, use your time and knees in a better way.

[459]

Politicians who feel that art is not a matter of politics make politics into an art.

I was sitting with Fancy on a bench on the outskirts of Haarlem. In the distance hobbled a little old woman. She kept bending down to pick up things which she collected in her apron. It was only little bits of wood she was looking for. . . .

Such poverty, I thought. And I calculated that soon she would pass by the bench I was sitting on, and I threw down a coin for her to pick up. And I was gladdened as each step brought her nearer to the gift I wanted to give her by chance. But comets and little old women who gather wood are one and the same thing. This comet described a different trajectory than I had calculated, and I feared that . . .

"My good woman!"

"What?"

"You are looking so diligently . . . I believe there's something lying there. . . ."

She didn't come closer, and went on looking for wood. Quite naturally. She was looking for wood under the trees, and what I wanted to point out to her was lying on the path. There was no wood there, as she well knew. Perhaps she thought I was mocking her.

"I mean, really, come now, in all truth . . . woman . . . come this way. I really believe that something is lying there . . . yes . . . it looks like money. . . ."

"Well, if you thought that's what it was you would have picked it up yourself!"

Then I picked up the coin and brought it over to her, and was saddened by the thought that this little old woman had hardly ever met any good people in her long life.

[505]

No one has a high enough estimation of what he could be, nor a low enough one of what he is.

[509]

Nothing is greater than the good. He who seeks to cap it with such words as *high, great, grand, exalted, noble,* etc., makes a verbal slip similar to those who say *rounder than a sphere*.

[510]

It's the same in fashion as in zoology. You often find those transitional types because Nature and tailors do not make large jumps.

[524]

The average level of readers is below the quality of the poorest writer.

[527]

He who applies himself to writing well can never produce much.

[530]

How Nature would laugh at us if she were conscious of our rage to categorize.

[541]

Truth is one and the number of untruths infinite.

[556]

He who communicates an untruth does not become poorer by a lie.

[567]

To doubt nothing is the surest way of never knowing anything.

[657]

The living are stoned with the laurelled skulls of the dead.

[684]

Whoever is unjust to others commits an injustice to himself because abuse of judgment is spiritual suicide.

[744]

There is an old grumbler in a German play who blames all mistakes, abuses and crimes on reading. His recurrent exclamation, *das kommt vom lesen!* [that's the result of reading], provides the play with its title and wit. Is the soup burned? . . . *das kommt vom lesen!* Is there, according to him, an error in the compass of his pupil's soul? . . *das kommt vom lesen!* Is he bothered by flies? . . *das kommt vom lesen!* Do his workers demand higher wages? . . . *Das kommt vom lesen!*

There is more truth in that farce than the writer himself was probably aware of. He who only wanted to make the penny gallery laugh about a *tic,* gave thinkers an excellent subject for study. Bothered by a host of abuses, I repeat after the old grumbler, in all seriousness, *das kommt vom lesen!*

The difference between us is primarily that he—a true OMAR*—wanted to have all books burned, while I urge an entirely different kind of enlightenment. I wish that people would read *well,* in order to *learn* how to read.

[747]

Ideas rule the world. Does it matter what the quality of these despots is? Nobody will affirm that it does.

I write this during the last days of July 1870. Soon,

---

* Concerning Omar, consider the following sentences from Multatuli's own note on the subject, added in 1876: "Probably for convenience sake, I stuck here to the accepted interpretation of this incident. You know that it has led to much controversy and that many respectable writers have absolved Caliph Omar from that book massacre. According to them it was the Christians who committed that crime, in particular a certain Archbishop Theophilus, during the reign of Theodosius the Great. For my part, I'll stick to Omar being the culprit, since it is generally known that Christians have never been guilty of crimes against civilization."

and for many years to come, anybody who has memorized his history lesson well will remember the great events which are about to happen, when he sees this date. More than a million people are getting ready to devour one another. The chassepots* will do wonders. The needle-rifle† will outdo the chassepot. The machinegun—a mechanical businesslike device for the promotion of space in the ranks of mankind—will put the chassepot and needle rifle to shame. Just so many individuals will be killed as can possibly be reconciled with the cowardice of war. The number of casualties will probably rise to *one-twentieth* of the number of soldiers who, as quickly as possible—withdrawing, outflanking, while covering a fortress, taking up positions, defending their lines, congregating at the rear—will flee in the theoretically proper way.

The battle will be bloody because the ratio of one dead to nineteen runaways is very much according to the tradition of official war heroes. I'll leave the question open whether one should grieve more over the one corpse or over the nineteen war experts who manage to save their precious lives for their country. Nor do we need to settle the matter. It's a sad affair, no matter how you look at it.

Sad! The grain is ripe and waits in vain for the sickle. Young daughters wait. Mothers wait. Civilization waits. All of Europe . . .

Oh well, all of that will be all right later on! Nature is too rich to go bankrupt, no matter what the losses.

---

* A chassepot was a breech-loading rifle that fired needles, adopted by the French army in 1866.
† Needle-rifles used a needle to explode the cartridge.

Just keep on waiting patiently, grain, mothers, young daughters and civilization. . . .

But in the meantime life is difficult for those who are not eternal and cannot wait. *"Don't erase my circles!"* cried Archimedes when Sicily was annexed by the Prussians of antiquity. Let me finish my ideas, O brave Romans of the no longer Holy German Empire!

And—yes, this above all—please don't eat up everything! Your heroic courage is *historical* . . . or so I am told, and I'll believe it. No better witnesses than the history books you yourself write. But, good god . . . how expensive everything is! Your courage devours everything, O very *historical* heroes, vegetables, beef, butter, *Ideeën,* lust for life, imagination, old-new herring, soul . . . everything!

You make it difficult for me to work. You who only kill—and only one in twenty at that, shame!—you bother me in my work . . . I who must create!

I see hundreds of oxen and thousands of soldiers streaming by my house. All of them have to go to the slaughter. Spurred on to enthusiasm by iron-tipped sticks in the hands of small boys, the oxen go their way silently. The soldiers—who or what spurs them on?—low all kinds of strange patriotic songs. The most stalwart Hindu would get an appetite for beef if he listened to the singing of these bipeds. Those sweet, sincere and silent oxen!

"I am a Prussian," asserts a Saxon.

"My colors are Prussian," answers a man from Nassau.

"They'll never get them," pledges a man from Hanover who is seeing the Rhine for the first time in his life, and had never tasted a drop of it.

"For the God who created iron ore . . ." gushes a
tailor from Hessen.

"Does not believe in slavery!" completes a grocery
boy from Frankfurt.

"Father, I call on Thee!" chants a Pole from the bor-
ders.

Again: sweet, sweet, genuine oxen!

Because . . . all that shouting is a lie!

Das kommt vom lesen!

And . . . everything is expensive. If you don't join
in the killing—or militarily run away, of course—you
cannot live.

The sole condition for prosperity is destruction.
There is no rest except at the price of savagery.

And all of Europe is waiting for the result of this
silly tragedy. Everywhere blockage, hindrance, disturb-
ance, obstruction, standstill. Everywhere unhappi-
ness . . . .

Das kommt vom lesen!

[785]

The entire morality of the world could perhaps be sum-
marized in the words, do as others do.

[795]

Some people still deal with their intelligence in the
same way some Catholics deal with their salvation.
"That's the business of the priest." Professors are paid
to be wise.

Just as in industry many appear to find it desirable to have a division of labor, so too in this business of religion people believe that the amassing of knowledge, the inquiry into the causes of things, can be left to precentors. According to this system, everybody else should be content making a catalogue of referrals or something like that.

Guilds are—not quite—abolished. Everyone yells and screams for free trade, open markets, free labor, emancipation. . . .

Everyone is exuberant in declarations of liberality.

And at the same time people are constantly shackling their minds by locking their desire to know, to understand and to do in the auditoriums of academe.

When you subcontract plowing, sewing, mowing, thrashing, even the grinding and baking . . .

Even including *eating* . . .

Remember that you will always remain responsible for your "own digestion," which made me so happy in [338], a text whose meaning I think I have made a little clearer here.

[816]

We resent others much more for knowing our faults than we resent ourselves for suffering them to exist.

[826]

Stains cannot be wiped off with a filthy rag.

What do we expect from teaching? What kind of instruction are we to give to the schoolmaster? After all,
the man has got to know what to stick to. From my
point of view, the answer to these questions isn't so
difficult. I feel that the capacity for thinking is primary,
and demand of the teacher—INDEPENDENT STUDY!
—that he . . .

Does the reader expect that here something like this
will follow: exercise in thinking, *a course in orthology,
instruction in intelligence?* Absolutely not! I purposely
chose those two terms because they carry the mark of
absurdity on their foreheads.

I demand of the teacher that he not *thwart* the exercise in thinking, which reveals itself just as naturally
as breathing. The young of the animal MAN will
think. That's the way it is because they are thinking
animals after all. And he who doubts this will be condemned to start a swimming school for ducklings. How
those ducks would fare if one made an expensive and
complicated study of what Nature gives freely and even
insists on, is their business. But, to be sure, the swimming would not become more perfect by forbidding the
chicks to go into the water and thereby *preventing* the
exercise.

Our teaching should not thwart thinking. It is not
so important what and how much we learn at school,
if only we do not *unlearn* how to learn.

It is true that, by itself, knowledge is a possession,
but it is our capacity for thought that provides us with
the means of obtaining that possession and, therefore,
is to the first as an orchard is to fruit. The most compe-

tent and most industrious master can impart only a little knowledge to his disciples, but this is completely irrelevant if he simply enables them—that is, if he continues to allow them—to keep on increasing that knowledge.

With a repeated appeal to [155] I want to point out here that the relative increase in knowledge which boys have when they leave school is very little in relation to that which they still have to learn, and imperceptibly proportionate to everything they will never learn. The distinction between *twenty* and *forty* cherries doesn't matter to the owner of the tree, especially not to the owner of the entire orchard if he learned well how to manage it, that is, again the comparison: if someone has not made him incompetent for such management.

The cramming of a little knowledge is detrimental. Not because of the knowledge, nor because it is a little bit, but because of the cramming.

[844]

The acknowledgment of ignorance appears to include an insult for the many who are content with partial knowledge.

[852]

One does not improve the swimming of ducks by throwing their eggs into the water.

I preach *dissatisfaction!* I maintain that it is a *duty* not to be satisfied with the way things are . . . things which would disgrace even the most malicious god.

Whoever thought that I support a *socialistic* or *communistic* upheaval understood me very badly. Precisely the opposite.

The French press of today, which is rotten in the most decent manner, pretends a horror of atheism. The men of the Commune* desecrate the churches, shoot priests, etc. Churches and priests represent, according to the narrow mind of the French newsmongers, Religion, and even God.

This is a general delusion, and perhaps also in this particular case. It may be that the Communards, like Elijah in 1 Kings 18, slaughter the priests in order to

---

* The Commune Multatuli is criticizing is the one Parisians organized in defiance of the national government, the Assembly, after France's defeat in the Franco-Prussian War (1870–71). The people of Paris had suffered more than the rest of France and had to accept a triumphal march of German troops into their city. Furthermore, Paris was in favor of a republic and diametrically opposed to the predominantly monarchist Assembly. Paris rebelled against the government but, to its misfortune, the Parisian workers were led by military and political incompetents. Hence the government had very little trouble defeating them. During the two months battle, atrocities were committed on both sides, but the government's revenge was worse than the Communards' trespasses: a conservative estimate is that more than twenty thousand men were killed in one week by reprisals. Being primarily a movement of oppressed and cheated workers—though admittedly a violent one —it is somewhat surprising that Multatuli is not taking their side; perhaps the governmental propaganda had done its work all too well.

please God,* but then this manifestation would testify to serious piety rather than to atheism. How much this applies to the Parisians I don't know. For the sake of convenience I will admit that these plunderers, robbers and murderers had disregarded all gods and were therefore, in the most literal sense of the word, *atheists*. In that case I would call them stupid. I blame them for not knowing the catechism of reasonable unbelief and, according to their actions, for being still tainted with the ridiculous prejudices left over from their churchgoing days.

Haven't they done—on a smaller scale and under circumstances which were far more enlightening—exactly the same thing that, only a few days later, without cause and with only a filthy desire for revenge, was done by the faithful believers? Shame on you, Parisian atheists, you have conducted yourselves like *Christians!* You who assume the honorific title of *atheist* have burned and killed like churchgoers, like vicious, pious ones, like Elijahs! You who pretended to have been called to the freedom of *Reason* have allowed yourself to go astray as if you were still bowed under the yoke of God! Shame! What's the use of discarding the bloody traditions of the personal Jehovah if we don't

---

* Elijah is the opponent of King Ahab who, under influence of his wife Jezebel, has allowed the religion of Baal to thrive in Israel. After a severe drought, Elijah challenges the priests of Baal to a duel of sacrifices. During this ceremony on Mt. Carmel the priests call on their god to ignite the wood under the sacrificial bullock, to no avail. Then Elijah has the altar and the animal drenched in water and calls upon his God who, in response, casts fire down. The people are convinced and at the prophet's command take the 450 priests of Baal down to a brook and kill them.

show *by our deeds* that we have become servants of the *nature of things,* which tells us so clearly what we should and shouldn't do! You combat tyranny and introduce oppression! You complain about abuse and then proceed to abuse! You shout for revenge because what's most essential is lacking and you disturb, lay waste and destroy! Shame!

Does nature command that? Is that a commandment of Reason?

Poor lost atheists of Paris, I advise you to go to school with reality, with common sense, with the truth which can be read in the Bible of facts. I assure you, I swear to you that violence . . .

Well, there is no need to swear an oath. Men without God in Paris were shot to death by men from Versailles with God on their side and this shows very clearly that religiosity is the gentlest thing in the world.

[919]

A hungry people is a barbaric people no matter how many thousands of prayers it might say, with or without making the sign of the cross.

[921]

Prophets establish Schools, but no prophet-school produces Seers.

[931]

The order of my *Ideeën* is not ruled by the presumptive
taste of my readers, but completely by the impressions
I have received, and according to the domestic claims
of my nature, which has had to deal with them. It is
impossible for me to change this method, and if I tried
to do so there soon would be no order to worry about,
for lack of *Ideeën*.

[935]

He who has to come up with principles in order to distinguish good from evil is a rogue.

[941]

To be fair, I have to admit that Darwin himself suffers
from the damned defect of halfheartedness. He ranks
far below his own system. I say this not only because
he accepts all kinds of things which haven't been
proved—and sometimes even things which have been
disproved—as the truth, but he doesn't dare break with
a God who, after all, according to that selfsame Darwinism, would not have a sphere of activity at all.
Doesn't he dare take on Anglicanism, the government's
famous high church? Poor science!

As far as I am concerned, I didn't get Darwinism
from Darwin. If people hadn't pursued and pestered
me as if I were a wild animal, I would have revealed
the main ingredient of his system long before he did.
His natural selection really does exist. But he attaches

a greater value to it than it deserves, because it's only
a subdivision of a much more general instinct. If people
don't make it completely impossible for me to work, I
hope to be able to demonstrate this at some time in the
future. For the moment, let me say only this: Darwin's
opinion about the influence of sexual choice limits the
solution of the means of evolution to those creatures
only who indeed *possess* a sex. For what is left of the
law when it is applied to the creation of sexless objects?
Or does he allow a God to take care of this category, a
God who creates suns and moons, marble and seawater,
but isn't to concern himself with the necks of giraffes
or the horns of cattle? To be blunt: Darwin is childish. . . .

[952]

Those who cackle about humility—always a *lie!*—may
give me a funny look about my self-congratulatory
tone. Despite themselves, however, they should *feel*
that there is a difference between empty bluster and
the rightful pride of the man who has kept on going
despite much sorrow. It is their own fault if they don't
feel this, which only gives me more cause to think myself superior. What's more, I have had and still do have
to think so. For it is only from this attitude that I
gather my strength to keep on going, and by doing so
I reveal my pride as a lesson to those few younger people who are worthy of suffering what I have suffered.

   Being incomplete, this lesson would be detrimental
if I didn't hasten to mention the very specific ingredient
which is the only one that justifies such pride and

makes it useful. That ingredient is *thought*. He who thinks cannot perish. He who thinks conquers. The primary consideration here is to use economically those tools which we need for this purpose. For the moment I'll ignore the relationship between careful thought and the ability to withstand the evils of the world. An attentive reader will find everywhere [in my work] evidence of my love for precision and my primary quest to find strength in it to bear my sorrow. This then explains my constant insistence on "the precise phrase" and on precision in "defining something."

[958]

The inhabitants of a certain island had destroyed all their locks centuries ago, so that even the memory of such things had been lost.

A traveller landed there who had a bunch of keys. He told them that, in his country with the help of keys rooms and closets could be locked, and how useful that was. The population listened to this revelation with admiration and . . . copied his keys. But they didn't see any of the results which he had praised so much.

People carried the keys around their necks, and there was just as much stealing from crates and closets as before. They hung them from branches . . . it didn't help. They buried them . . . the same result. A wise man suggested that they rattle the keys. That night the beard was stolen from his chin. The priests thought of a new way. Two keys, put crosswise on the possessions one wanted to keep, would scare off the thieves. The godless villains paid no attention to the holy symbol.

Don't you think it's a pity that they had forgotten to ask the stranger how exactly one should use such useful things, to prevent them from being totally useless?

After much thought some people began to realize that not all keys can be used in every country. A philosopher remembered having heard from his grandmother —the old drudge must have gotten it, like other senators, from John Stuart Mill—that one must have "original" keys. All the smiths went to work! The fellows who had . . . translated the strange keys weren't allowed to participate. The others feared that they would let themselves be guided by their memory of the models. The task of those poor smiths was very difficult. The keys had to be exactly like those of the stranger but—probably because of the contemplated "originality"—completely different.

When someone displayed an instrument that looked like one of the strange keys, he was stoned because his work had an exotic tinge to it. And when someone made a key that didn't have the slightest resemblance to the strange objects, he was stoned because he dared to deviate from the foreign masters.

Now they did succeed in exterminating all the smiths, but the desired goal of making useful keys remained an unfinished item on their long list of stupid wishes.

The kind stranger, who seemed to travel around the world to say a true word here and there, let a storm cast him once more onto their shore.

All of them met him with the greeting, "Your keys are no good!" This was somewhat true, but . . . only half true, and therefore, considering everything, not true. The keys were no good for *them*. Whether they were all that useful in the stranger's country, as he assured them, isn't our problem. We have to deal with the islanders who stoned their smiths.

"Your keys are no good! Look at all the *tumuli** that cover the pitiful remains of the wretched ones who were deceived by your models. How do the smiths in your country fare who are charged with the production of a key?"

"They measure the lock which has to fit the key, and then . . ."

"A lock? What's that?"

Dear compatriots, as long as you don't have locks which have to fit dramatic—and other!—literature, no smith will be able to come up with an original key to your esthetic sensibility.

[1051b]

He who loses sight of the material meaning of the ideal is a slovenly housekeeper.

[1051c]

The awe inspired by how things sound plays a very large role in the history of delusions, if not the starring role. As soon as the disseminators of a misconception have succeeded in stamping their theories with a strange name, then that name will live longer than the original faith in the reasoning that engendered it.

* Latin for "tombs."

The adult who was sitting by himself had looked up stealthily for a moment when Wouter came in, eyed him with that strange expression of animosity towards strangers which separates man so unfavorably from several other types of animals and which we can particularly observe in savages, children and . . . some women. The unspoken, "Who are you?" has on such occasions the same force as a declaration of war.

We can observe this phenomenon daily in children, and I believe that it is unknown to only a few. To observe it among the human specimens who are explicitly called "savages" in the geography textbooks, the European has to travel. Concerning the third type of individuals who are guilty of this specifically human absurdity . . . we have only to pay attention to the glances with which "ladies," when they meet each other in the street, display this characteristic of their all too primitive humanity. They measure each other, weigh each other, judge, assess, condemn and damn each other. This shows us that the fangs of cannibalism haven't completely fallen out. Let us assume that sweet Nature ordained all of this so we wouldn't be too haughty to dogs and angels. Nature preserved these rudiments of a long gone period of our evolution as if to call out to us, "Don't forget that you were once like this. You can see for yourself that if Mrs. A, B, C etc., didn't have silk dresses on and gentlemen by their sides they would devour each other."

It's possible, of course, that those ladies aren't quite all that bad and that a few would refrain from anthropophagy even if they didn't have gentlemen or silk.

I have observed this mene-mene-tekel fury in gentle creatures who, under normal circumstances, really wouldn't be capable of devouring a live rabbit. But to give this gentleness no more credit than it is due, we shouldn't lose sight of the fact that such a little animal was never guilty of . . . indeed, guilty of what?

For what is in fact the crime committed by a lady who meets other ladies when she's taking a walk? Her crime? Well, one doesn't know her. Isn't that unforgivable? She dares to exist, to be there, to walk, to breathe, even to wear a particular dress and . . . one doesn't know her!

The fact that sometimes the ribbons of Mrs. A are not approved by Miss B can be explained. It is excusable that the hat of Miss C is not to the taste of Miss D. It's understandable that the Widow E would have chosen an entirely differently striped material than the one Miss F appears to want to be so exceptionally pretty in today . . . but still, is there any reason in all of this to look at each other so furiously and not quite bite each other?

This: "I don't know you; hence, an enemy!" reveals a particular conception of humanity. Perhaps I unfairly called it primitive. It does seem to date from the time when we lived in caves and trees, but we can suppose that it was preceded by other, more gentle habits. Perhaps this small-town barbarism was once a novelty and was palmed off as civilization. It points to a tribal community which was the result of friction, to adaptation which went hand in hand with isolation, to a lack of foods which made every stranger look like an intruder, a conqueror, a thief. It had to be different at one time, because our savages, ladies, and children are not quite unadulterated primitives, either. The family tree of their cruel shyness climbs at most up to the troglodytes but certainly not up to paradise.

[1060a]

In spite of our attachment to the familiar we are possessed by a yearning and a drive to elevate everything that is strange and unusual. Since we are at the same time wanderers and homebodies, we adore what restricts us and shrink from what has been praised as soon as it deviates from those things we condemn ourselves, but which chain us with the fetters of habit. Our lauding and praising of the unfamiliar is common to certain reformers, and not only the most narrow-minded ones. In this they resemble the oyster who sang of the eagle's flight. The beast rhymed so beautifully that Jupiter sent him a pair of wings and offered to turn him into a bird. But the singer declined that distinction because it would be a pity to leave his shell, in which he couldn't store wings.

[1065]

A sixth continent exists which has not yet found its Columbus. And this is all the more strange since thousands upon thousands purport to be taking great pains to discover it. This continent is man. We do not know him.

[1076]

The alleged preference for work other than that which has been issued to us is quite often dislike for all work.

[1078]

The youthful Lacrymax* received the light of day from a family which, since time immemorial, had dealt in utility. Lacrymax's birth was an example of this, since his entire creation was nothing but a matter of social utility. The advertisement which announced his humanization could really have been formulated as follows: "Today was successfully delivered a dose of general welfare, etc." But the birth of the utility child was not announced in this manner because his parents, along with all their other virtues, also possessed the very profitable quality of humility. The curious newspaper reader was only informed that a child had been born, that's all.

Ten, twelve, twenty years later there were wondrous discussions about Lacrymax's career. As with all proper parents, utility stood at the top of the list of desiderata. Money? No one thought of it, that is, nobody said a word about it.

One of the members of the family proposed to define the concept "utility" more precisely. He thought that the sense of the word was too general. How can you obtain a patent as general-utility-manufacturer? Everybody understood that it was necessary to choose a particular specialty. But . . . which one?

* The name is coined from the Latin verb *lacrimare* ("to cry").

The fashions of the time included chastity. It's neither here nor there whether this fashion was also for the family Lacrymax a result of higher food prices. But what can be said with certainty is that the word "virtue" in Lacrymaxian meant little more than maimed sexuality and that "vice" meant the opposite. Easy as pie.

The curtailing of *that* vice and the encouragement of *that* virtue was therefore the specialized utility practiced by the Lacrymax family and the young Lacrymax, therefore, was also to dedicate himself to that end. When he was ten years old, he already knew by heart long poems against lustfulness. One of these, and the most beautiful one, ended: "And the emaciated corpse sinks clattering into the grave!"

Everybody knows that elderly virgins of both sexes, ascetics, meat killers, heroes who succumb either to bullets or endless garrison duty, workmen who fall from scaffolds, people suffering from cholera and tuberculosis, Origeneans, Josephs of Egypt, Charles Grandisons, Good Eggs,*—in short, all chaste corpses —never sink into the grave unless they are blushing, completely unemaciated and without clattering . . . if they sink into the grave at all, which is at their own discretion.

* Origen was an early Church Father (A.D. 185–254). He carried piety to a certain extreme when, as a young man, he took rather literally the Gospel, "and there be eunuchs, which have made themselves eunuchs for the kingdom of heaven's sake" (Matt. 19:12), and castrated himself. He died from injuries sustained from torture.

Charles Grandison, hero of Samuel Richardson's epistolary novel *The History of Sir Charles Grandison* (1754), was a typically brave and morally pure character.

Be that as it may, the eternal blush of "virtue" is well known, hence it is quite superfluous to write books about casuistry, or discourses concerning the basis of morality. The question, what is good and what is not good? seems too simple to me for discussion. The whole business depends on the degree of emaciation and the *only* criterion for human worth is a pair of scales. The reader will thank me, I hope, for this simplification of the method of appraising mores. My claim to gratitude is even greater because personally I am quite skinny and look like a walking corpse. And so I preach against my parish and gain faith.

We don't waste any time with such boorish observations as, for example, the fact that an industrious life of the soul, vexation or weariness from the struggle against evil, etc., etc., could well produce symptoms which prepare someone a little too soon for "sinking with a clatter into the grave." Nor do I allow myself the time to plea for the immense difference between singing the praises of lust and the condemnation of middle-class narrow-mindedness, which slaps its little virtues together solely with materials from this subordinate component of human existence. For the moment let it suffice that the lachrymatory family belonged heart and soul to the latter category. Virtue or chastity, it was all the same to them. They didn't know, comprehend, or respect anything else.

But there are specializations even in chastity. On this occasion the young Lacrymax exhibited a particular preference for fallen girls or, more precisely, for "uplifting" such people. But . . . in order to lift up fallen girls, you need to stand. In order to stand, you have to live, eat, drink, be housed. Moreover, there are fallen girls whom you cannot properly lift up unless you enable them also to live, eat, drink, be housed, etc. And for this you need . . . money!

Money?

But our Lacrymax wasn't concerned with that. Really he wasn't.

"Utility, gentlemen, utility . . ."

You won't find here the wondrous discourses concerning utility which some people would give on such an occasion.

But . . . money was necessary! To deny this fact would be foolish. All the fallen girls were waiting to get up until Lacrymax could earn enough money to reach them a helping hand. . . .

The good fellow couldn't take it any longer. He looked for and found a profession which enabled him within a few years to satisfy his hunger for utility. . . .

Our Lacrymax started a good whorehouse.

[1095]

To call the "masses" stupid is probably to be just as inaccurate as to think that *five* is lovable or *air* triangular. The "masses" as such do not think and, therefore, cannot think incorrectly. They are pushed in a certain direction or remain lying in chains, depending upon whether this is desired by certain individuals or brought about by a set of circumstances. Their main characteristic, both when standing still and when in motion, is inertia.

[1104]

The civilizing influence of so-called classical studies reveals itself—unless it stays away completely—only
later in life. In the beginning the result of having made
Cicero's acquaintance is cannibalistic. One has to get
through it, so it seems, but it's a pity.

What played the role for the Greeks that the classics play for us?

Do the Greeks perhaps have the distinction of being
precursors precisely because they did not choose precursors for models and were therefore forced to be
themselves?

It's worth the bother to think about this.

[1109]

Much practice in comprehension is needed to realize
how some people are capable of understanding.

[1111]

Magnanimity is a sweet you should nibble at just as
little as at any other candy.

[1123]

Logical necessity does not let itself be ruled by the fingers or claws of gods and devils.

[1126]

Plato once had a bad cold and showed it. Thersites imitated his cough and asked: "Am I not like Plato now?"

Which wasn't the worst, because one is free to ask such a question. The worst was that thousands upon thousands answered: "Exactly! Long live Thersites, the new philosopher."

The man founded a school.

And therefore: *cave, caveto, caveto, cavete, cavetote, caveunto!**

[1163]

Sorrow and happiness depend more on what they are than on what happens to us.

[1181]

It is just as impossible to produce something good by following models as it is to feed oneself with the food someone else has eaten.

[1186a]

An impossible duty is not a duty, and the striving after it stands in the way of fulfilling our real duties.

* A declension of a Latin verb meaning "to watch out": hence, you watch out, he watches out (twice), you (plural) shall watch out, they shall watch out—of which the latter two forms are very pedantic.

[1186b]

It is easier to imagine floating above a far distant mountain than to pick up one's foot to step over a pebble in reality.

[1193a]

No one is bored without being ashamed. One doesn't like to be caught at it, from which we might possibly draw the conclusion that one isn't allowed to be bored.

[1193e]

The worst trials are visited upon us by trivial things. They attack us daily, incessantly and tenaciously, and usually find us unprepared. Furthermore, there is no honor to be gained in such a battle. Moses and the "Lord" knew what they were doing. They didn't plague Egypt with tigers but with grasshoppers.

[1200]

What appears to us to be important in antiquity, or romantic in the Middle Ages, was once quite commonplace.

[1209a]

A pearl diver does not fear the mud.

Reader, I am dead. Some weeks ago I attended a lecture on The Essence of the Flame, and the lecturer, a doctor of chemistry, began with the assurance that some characteristics of the flame were already known to the Ancients. I know that similar incidents served as material for anecdotes many years ago, and it wouldn't surprise me if people looked upon this exordium of my obituary as a warmed-over pleasantry. To that I answer with the serious assurance that I tell the truth, and find the attacks on me remarkable precisely *because* they have, for so long, served as fillers in bad comedies. A charitable coughing fit kept me from shouting at the talented and recently matriculated speaker: "That's right, Doc, and the same thing goes for the onion!" But I would have been wrong. The man was deadly serious and made me realize once again that I had spoken the truth when, in my disquisition on Free Study, I argued that a hunter of anecdotes can never dream up any foolishness that doesn't have its counterpart in reality.

All right then, reader, I am dead, and want to tell you how this transformation of my social condition came about. Even the Ancients knew about death. Some of their philosophers had already understood that one can die in several ways. It was reserved for our century, however, and, more precisely, for me, to discover that one can die from a couple of dozen magazines and lectures which inform you about literature. . . .

In my capacity as deceased writer I am incapable of expressing myself clearly. This peculiarity of death was also known to the Ancients. One even finds traces of people who didn't utter a word after they had died, but this was an exception that can be proven by those who were at Emmaus and by anyone who had read the thirty-first chapter of Philostratus' *Life of Apollonius of Tyane.** If the reader doesn't know this book, then I choose not to have anything to do with him. As a classical writer I have a right—and I insist on it—to an audience that has at least a little knowledge of the old models. I can't cast my discourse before ignorant people. When I wrote my *Idee* 13, I was still alive. Just consider, reader, how difficult it is for me to report with accuracy the events that were caused by my death, when I already had trouble expressing myself in a manner approximating precision when I was still alive! No matter what ideas one harbors about death—the word "harbor" is again drawn after a model—*how* one thinks about it, no one will deny that it usually has the effect of hampering speech. I therefore beg your forgiveness if I am less clear in this chapter than I was wont to be when I was alive. If by accident I come alive again, I will keep my thoughts as close to the ground as possible, so they can entice the slowest turtle to play a nice game of leapfrog. . . .

* The reference to Philostratus is puzzling; his *Life of Apollonius of Tyana* has five "books," hence has five chapters 31. But none of these contain any material that can possibly be construed to have anything to do with mortality. Despite protestations about his scholarship, I suspect that Multatuli was overreaching here—as he did in other places.